THREE IMPERIAL MATHEMATICIANS

The NEW HORIZON series

EDWARD ROSEN

THREE IMPERIAL MATHEMATICIANS:

KEPLER TRAPPED BETWEEN TYCHO BRAHE AND URSUS

New York
ABARIS BOOKS, INC.

International Standard Book Number 0-89835-242-8
First published 1986 by Abaris Books, Inc.
24 West 40th Street, New York, New York 10018
Printed in the United States of America

To Sandra and Carla

CONTENTS

ABBREVIATIONS

Dreyer	J.L.E. Dreyer, *Tycho Brahe* (Edinburgh, 1890; reprint, New York, 1963)
DSB	*Dictionary of Scientific Biography*, 16 vols (New York, 1970-1980)
F	*Joannis Kepleri astronomi opera omnia*, ed. Christian Frisch, 8 vols (Frankfurt a.M. / Erlangen, 1858-1871); reprint, Hildesheim, I (1971), II (1977)
Gruner	Edmund Reitlinger, C.W. Neumann, and C. Gruner, *Johannes Kepler* (Stuttgart, 1868)
GW	Johannes Kepler, *Gesammelte Werke* (Munich, 1937–)
Hansch	Michael Gottlieb Hansch, ed. *Epistolae ad J. Kepplerum* (Leipzig, 1718)
JHA	*Journal for the History of Astronomy*
List-Bialas	Martha List and Volker Bialas, "Die Coss von Jost Bürgi in der Redaktion von Johannes Kepler," Bayerische Akademie der Wissenschaften, mathematischnaturwissenschaftliche Klasse, Abhandlungen, neue Folge, Heft 154, 1973
NCCW	*Nicholas Copernicus Complete Works*, I (New York/London, 1972); II, *Revolutions*, translated by Edward Rosen, with commentary (Baltimore, 1978); III, Minor Works (1985)
PS	Ptolemy, *Syntaxis*
StC	*Studia Copernicana* series (Wrocław/Cracow/Gdańsk/ Warsaw, 1970 –).
TB	*Tychonis Brahe Dani opera omnia*, 15 vols (Copenhagen, 1913-1929)
TCT	Edward Rosen, *Three Copernican Treatises*, 3rd ed. (New York, 1971)
UAH	Nicholas Reimers Ursus, *De astronomicis hypothesibus* (Prague, 1597)

UFA	Ursus, *Fundamentum astronomicum* (Strasbourg, 1588)
Zinner	Ernst Zinner, *Geschichte und Bibliographie der astronomischen Literatur in Deutschland zur Zeit der Renaissance*, 2nd ed. (Stuttgart, 1964)
□	denotes illustration corresponding to the number in the margin

Dr. Edward Rosen died on 28 March 1985 before he could see this book through the press. The index and bibliography were completed by Dr. Erna Hilfstein and Sandra Rosen.

INTRODUCTION

Dithmarschen, for centuries a small but prosperous peasant republic in western Holstein, was overrun in 1559 by three allied neighboring powers. One of the trio, the kingdom of Denmark, annexed its prearranged share, to be administered by the royal governor of Holstein, Heinrich Rantzau, an instigator of the conquest. An experienced diplomat, soldier, and administrator, Rantzau was also a prolific author, an avid collector of a famous library of 6,300 volumes, and an eager patron of learning. His new Dithmarschen subjects included an eight-year old boy in an illiterate swineherd's family in Hennstedt [then called Henstede]. Had a system of free, universal education prevailed at that time, this youngster's innate ability would have been discovered and encouraged. Nevertheless, the boy, Nicholas Reimers, used his spare time, while tending pigs, to teach himself to read by the age of eighteen. In the same way he learned Latin, then the indispensable approach to a professional career. He also mastered classical Greek, French, and the mathematical sciences. As an extraordinary autodidact, he gained Rantzau's favor. To show his gratitude, in 1580 Reimers entitled his Latin grammar *Grammatica Latina Ranzoviana*. While living in Rantzau's residence in Hattstedt [formerly Hattstede] as the official surveyor, on 14 September 1583 Reimers completed a short work on that subject in the German language. He named it

Geodaesia Ranzoviana, and dedicated it to Rantzau.

A year later Reimers was in the service of Eric Lange, a Danish nobleman with an atypical passion for matters of the mind. Lange was a kinsman of the illustrious Tycho Brahe, the outstanding astronomer of the age. The king of Denmark had granted Brahe the island Hven in the Danish Sound. There Brahe had constructed two splendid observatories, equipped with huge observational instruments and staffed by expert assistants. Brahe was not satisfied to be, and to be recognized as, the preeminent astronomical observer before the invention of the telescope. He knew that the dominant astronomical system of antiquity, formulated by Claudius Ptolemy in the second century of the Christian era, suffered from serious defects. Brahe was also intimately familiar with the astronomical system that had recently been propounded by Nicholas Copernicus in 1543. In opposition to the Ptolemaic system, whose earth remained motionless in the center of the universe, Copernicus proclaimed that the earth was a planet, revolving once a year around the sun. Although Brahe admired the achievement of Copernicus, whom he honored as a second Ptolemy, he could not accept Copernicus's moving earth. A fierce theological controversy was then raging in Denmark concerning these theories. In the eyes of the dominant ecclesiastical party, a moving earth contradicted Sacred Scripture. Brahe had enemies enough without tackling the fundamentalist theologians. His foes were numerous in Copenhagen at the royal court, elsewhere in Denmark among his peers, in the international scholarly world, as well as at home on Hven, where his feudal subjects were disgruntled. Besides, according to the theory then in vogue, earth was the heaviest of the four elements, and therefore unsuited for motion. Dissatisfaction with both the Ptolemaic and Copernican systems impelled Brahe, after an intense intellectual effort, to devise his own, the Tychonic, system.

In 1584, when Lange decided to visit Brahe, his friend and kinsman, Reimers insisted on accompanying him. While on Hven, during two weeks in September, Reimers continued his self-education. He was accused of surreptitiously copying unpublished material lying about, charges he hotly denied: he argued he was merely sketching the buildings. After Lange's party returned home, Reimers's behavior became intolerably psychopathic, and Lange was obliged to dismiss him.

Thereafter, Reimers asserts, in the home of a Pomeranian nobleman in Poland close to the Pomeranian border, having reread Copernicus a little more carefully, on 1 October 1585 he thought out his new cosmic system. So equipped, Reimers turned his thoughts to Kassel, where the Landgrave of Hesse maintained an observatory and a talented staff. On his way to Kassel, in Magdeburg, Reimers called on the rector of the local school, George Rollenhagen, a leading German poet, astronomer-astrologer, and friend of Rantzau. In the course of their conversation Reimers disclosed his new cosmic system (which was the Tychonic system, slightly modified by incorporation of Copernicus's daily rotation of the earth). Reimers then proceeded to Kassel, where on 1 May 1586 he revealed his cosmology. The Landgrave was so impressed that he ordered his technician to demonstrate the new system by means of a small planetarium. But Reimers aroused the suspicions of the Landgrave's astronomer.

Meanwhile, on Hven, Brahe was engaged in printing on his own press his book about the spectacular comet of 1577. Something suddenly caused him to expand the book. Fear of plagiarism induced him to insert hurriedly a brief account of his world system in the lengthy book about the comet, without bothering to build a smooth connection between the two disparate discussions. In May 1588 Brahe sent his comet book to friends, including Rantzau. Highly sensitive to novel scientific developments, Rantzau immediately recognized the importance of Brahe's new world system. He extracted it, and dispatched copies to several astronomers.

Rollenhagen responded that the hypotheses had been imparted to him in Magdeburg in 1586. His report was promptly transmitted by Rantzau to Brahe.

Unable to remain in Kassel, Reimers moved on to Strasbourg in the summer of 1587. There, on 31 July 1588, having adopted the additional surname Ursus (the Bear), he published his *Foundation of Astronomy*, in which he claimed Brahe's hypotheses, somewhat altered, as his own innovation. Pleading destitution, Reimers Ursus dedicated each of the twenty-one diagrams in his *Foundation of Astronomy* to a potential sponsor. The stratagem succeeded, and in the summer of 1591 Ursus was appointed Imperial Mathematician of the Holy Roman Empire. Emperor Rudolph II was an ardent devotee of astrology, and the principal task of his Imperial Mathematician was the preparation of horoscopes. In the case of Rudolph's older brother, who died on 12 February 1595, Ursus had guessed right. But about a certain Wallachian prince he guessed wrong, and failed to withstand examination by the emperor. Hence Ursus turned against astrology, which he denounced as a deception, although his praise of it had preceded his appointment as Imperial Mathematician.

Ursus was reviled with the utmost contempt as a plagiarist by Brahe and the Landgrave's mathematician in their correspondence, as published in Tycho's *Astronomical Letters*, dedicated in Hven on 21 March 1596. Determined to respond, Ursus immediately applied for the requisite publication privilege, tantamount to copyright. But the tone of his *Astronomical Hypotheses*, printed early in 1597 in Prague, the imperial capital, was so vicious that no censor would have approved it. Hence it was published without the imperial privilege. The printer's name was withheld, and the book was available from Ursus himself.

To demonstrate how highly regarded he was outside Brahe's circle, Ursus included in his *Astronomical Hypotheses* a letter written to him in 1595 by the teacher of mathematics in Graz, the capital of the Austrian province of Styria. This young instructor, recently appointed Provincial Mathematician of Styria, who believed he had solved the "cosmographic mystery," was preparing it for publication. As a beginner, he wanted to ascertain the Imperial Mathematician's reaction to his discovery, which he summarized in his letter. With insincere flattery and without any inkling of the acrimonious controversy over priority, he blurted out to Ursus: "I love your hypotheses." The Imperial Mathematician had not sought permission to publish this letter in his *Astronomical Hypotheses*, nor did he notify the author of the letter that he had published it. He also took good care not to send a copy of his *Astronomical Hypotheses*, containing the printed letter, to its author, none other than Johannes Kepler.

Young Kepler's position at Graz was not a happy one. The spectre of religious persecution in Styria hung ominously over him. He sought desperately to escape. One possibility was Brahe. The Danish astronomer recognized at once the intellectual virtuosity of Kepler's *Cosmographic Mystery*, although he disagreed with it wholeheartedly. Yet, Brahe was emotionally mature enough to realize that Kepler had unwittingly put his foot in a bear trap with his indiscreet letter to Ursus. Overlooking Kepler's misstep, Brahe tried to attract the younger man to his staff.

Meanwhile Brahe attacked Ursus with every weapon at his disposal. Ursus's professorship at the University of Prague was declared vacant. His *Astronomical Hypotheses* was banned; all copies were ordered surrendered to the authorities to be burned. Ursus fled from Prague, and was replaced by Brahe as Imperial Mathematician. To consolidate his case against his predecessor, Brahe gathered legal depositions from witnesses. He likewise ordered Kepler, who had joined his team, to compose a *Defense of Tycho against Ursus.* This remarkable essay, the earliest exploration of the history and logical structure of astronomical hypotheses, was not quite finished when Brahe died on 24 October 1601. Two days later, Kepler was appointed Imperial Mathematician.

This fascinating story of three Imperial Mathematicians has been recalled many times, but has never been explored in depth, as it is in this book, as far as possible in the very words of the protagonists themselves. The bulk of the press run of Ursus's *Astronomical Hypotheses* was seized in the home of his widow, who was promised 300 florins as compensation. The elimination of the edition was so nearly complete that the foremost biographer of Brahe was unable to consult a copy. On the basis of the limited evidence accessible to him, in the matter of the priority dispute, he drew the wrong conclusion. This has since been reiterated time and time again, and it is still being repeated. A thorough examination of this complex and intriguing entanglement, however, is provided for the first time in the present volume.

Ursus's *Fundamentum astronomicum* was published in Strasbourg in 1588 by a highly respected and immensely productive printer. Yet the recent authoritative census of books published in Alsace during the sixteenth century and preserved in the national and university library of Strasbourg does not include Ursus's *Fundamentum astronomicum*. As for his *De hypothesibus astronomicis* that was banned and ordered burned, the command was carried out so thoroughly that very few copies have survived. Photographic facsimiles of both of these rare books were kindly supplied by the Royal Library in Copenhagen, to which I wish to extend my sincere thanks.

Edward Rosen

I

BRAHE'S PUBLICATION OF HIS HYPOTHESIS

1. Tycho Brahe (1546-1601), Imperial Mathematician from 1599 to 1601

I

BRAHE'S PUBLICATION OF HIS HYPOTHESIS

Tycho Brahe□ (1546-1601) was one of the greatest 1
observational astronomers of all time.□ Some people 2
think he was the greatest. But his innovation and skill in observing were not ends in themselves. Their ultimate purpose was to reveal the hidden structure of the universe. This secret had not been revealed, he felt, by the cosmologies he had learned as a student. Conscious of their defects, he devised his own hypothesis, the Tychonic system.

Two major celestial events shaped his thinking: the new star of 1572 and the brilliant comet of 1577. Around these spectacular heavenly displays he planned a comprehensive work in three volumes. Of these, the earliest to be published was the second: *Recent Phenomena in the Celestial World, Book II, about the brilliant comet* (stella caudata) *which was seen from about the end of the* [first] *third of November in the year 1577 to the end of January in the following* [year]. In the place of Brahe's exceedingly long title, a short title is preferable for easy reference. Since Brahe often called this work his "comet" book, *Stella caudata* (The
Star with a Tail) will serve as the short title here.□ 3

2. Brahe's Observatories: (A) Uraniburg; (B) Wandsbek; (C) Benátky; (D) Imperial Gardens, Prague; (E) Jacob Kurtz's House, Prague

TYCHONIS BRAHE DANI

DE

MVNDI AETHEREI

RECENTIORIBVS

PHAENOMENIS

LIBER SECVNDVS

QVI EST DE ILLVSTRI STELLA CAVDATA
ab elapſo ferè triente Nouembris Anni 1577, vſq;
in finem Ianuarij ſequentis
conſpecta.

3. Title Page of Brahe's *Stella caudata*, Uraniburg, 1588

The printing of *Stella caudata*, as originally planned in eight chapters, began in 1587. But something happened that made Brahe change his plan. He increased the number of chapters to ten, with Chapter X of the published version corresponding to what had been the eighth and final chapter of the original version. In its place Chapter VIII of the published version set forth Brahe's hypothesis. This is on the face of it an intrusion in *Stella caudata*. It is not smoothly linked with what precedes and follows it. *Stella caudata* was printed on Brahe's own press in his own observatory, Uraniburg,
on the island of Hven in the Danish Sound.□ Why did 4
he suddenly interrupt the printing process and recast *Stella caudata* so that its Chaper VIII hastily presented in a brief and general form the hypothesis he had

intended to publish much later in full detail? As he recalled the situation a decade later,

> Having devised the system of hypotheses long before, I would not have inserted it in my book on the comet of the year [15]77 had I not been afraid of such plagiarists, to whom it had become known in my establishment.[1]

TOPOGRAPHIA INSVLÆ VENVSIÆ, VULGO HVENNÆ.

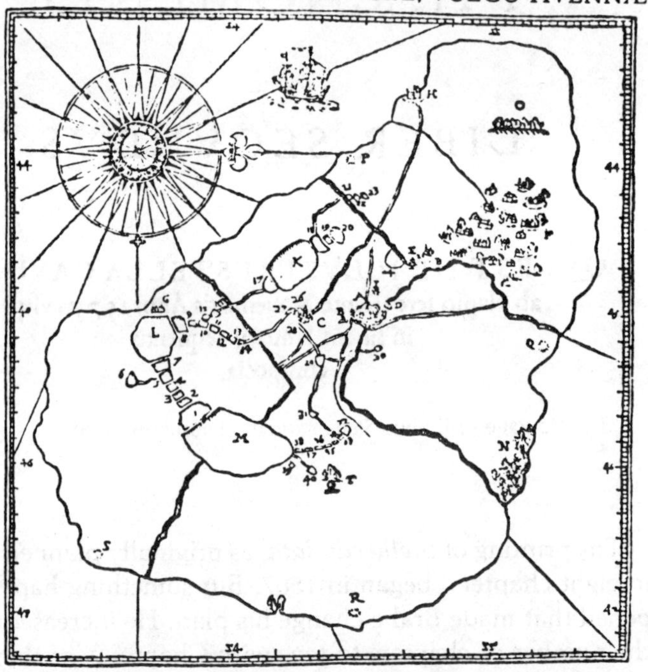

4. Hven, Brahe's Island in the Danish Sound

When the printing of *Stella caudata* was finished, Brahe sent copies in May 1588 to some friends, in-
5 cluding Heinrich Rantzau□ (1526-1599), the royal governor of Holstein in the kingdom of Denmark. In western Holstein Rantzau had participated in the conquest of Dithmarschen, of which he wrote an account under the pseudonym Cilicius Cimber (Basel, 1570).[2]

5. Heinrich Rantzau (1526-1599) aged 71; painted in 1596; engraving by Johann Benjamin Brühl (1691-1763)

But his military and administrative activities were
overshadowed by his devotion to culture. His library
became famous, and he won renown as a patron of
learning. Recognizing the importance of Brahe's
hypothesis, Rantzau asked the author for additional
copies, and Brahe sent him five.[3] Excerpting Chapter
VIII, Rantzau transmitted it to a number of astronomers. Two of them reacted by raising questions about
Brahe's hypothesis in their replies to Rantzau, who
continued to serve as a message center by relaying
their doubts to Brahe. One of these critics was well
known to him, the other not at all. The familiar
6 figure, Caspar Peucer□ (1525-1602), had been a professor under whom Brahe had studied more than two
7 decades earlier at the University of Wittenberg,□ in
1566. After receiving an excerpt of his former professor's reply to Rantzau, on 13 September 1588 Brahe
wrote to Peucer:

> In response to the request of my dear friend, the most noble Heinrich Rantzau, I sent him several copies of my work on *Recent Phenomena in the Celestial World, Book II.* I understand that he excerpted the exposition of the hypothesis which is found there in Chapter VIII,[4] and sent it to you and other scholars in Germany.[5]

Later on in this very long letter to Peucer, Brahe referred to the other German astronomer who had replied to Rantzau and whose name he had not previously known:

> A certain other astronomer, unknown to me, likewise had a certain other doubt about this arrangement in my hypothesis. He too wrote about it to the most noble lord Heinrich Rantzau, pointing out that the hypotheses had been imparted to him two years earlier by a certain runaway employee of mine.[6]

On the same day on which Brahe wrote to Peucer, he enclosed a copy of his Peucer letter in a communica-

20.
BILTNVS DES H:H:
D: CAS PARIS
PEV CERI
Ætatis suæ 48
15 75
WVNDER WER HIE ZV SAGEN GLEICH
DAS GOT DISN MAN BEGABT SO REICH
MIT VIELEN KVNSTEN AVSERKORN
IN WELCHEN ER WER DOCTOR WORN
ABER ALLEIN INNDR ARCZENEI
LEST ER SICH SCHELTEN E! DOCtor Frei

6. Caspar Peucer (1525-1602), Brahe's teacher at the University of Wittenberg; imaginative portrait, made in 1575 by Baltasar Jenichen

tion to Rantzau. In it he referred to the doubts about his hypothesis raised by "that other astronomer, of uncommon ability as it appears, George Rullenhagen (although his name had not previously been known to me)."[7] Brahe's unfamiliarity with George Rollenhagen□ (1542-1609) is apparent in his misspelling of the surname as Rullenhagen four times in this 8
letter of 13 September 1588 to Rantzau.

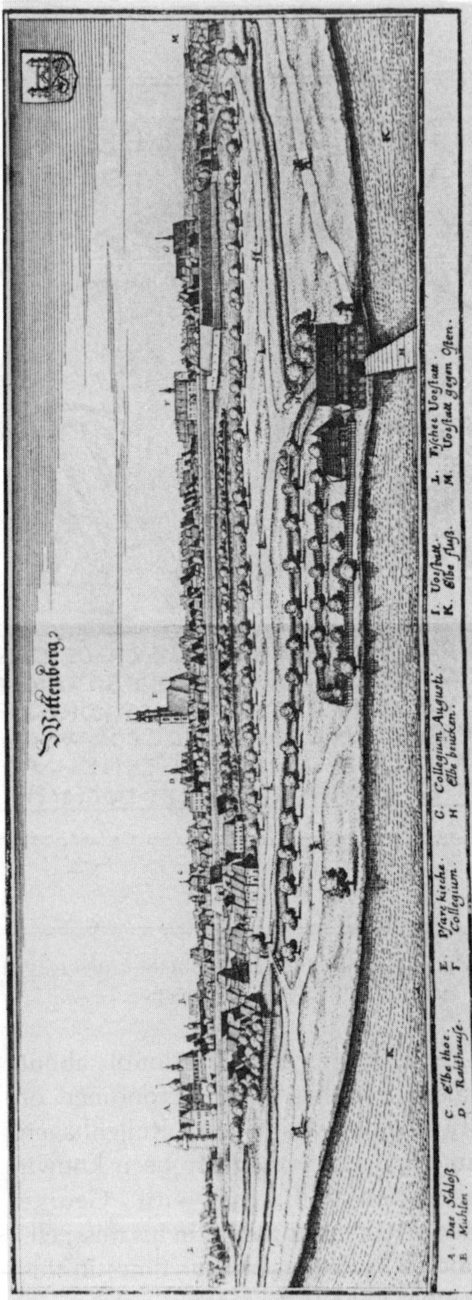

7. Wittenberg, after a pen and ink sketch by Wilhelm Dilich (1571/72-1650)

8. George Rollenhagen (1542-1609), satirist, author of *The Battle of the Frogs and the Mice*

Unfortunately we do not have Rollenhagen's letter, written well before 13 September 1588, in which he told Rantzau that Brahe's hypothesis had been communicated to him two years earlier, in 1586. Nor do we have Rantzau's letter promptly transmitting this news to Brahe, who was astounded, since none of his employees had ever run away. Nobody had left his tight little island of Hven without his knowledge or permission. Worst of all, he had not been aware that on 31 July 1588 Nicholas Reimers Ursus of Dithmarschen (1551-1600) had published in Strasbourg his
9 *Foundation of Astronomy*,□ claiming as his own a slightly modified form of Brahe's hypothesis.[8]

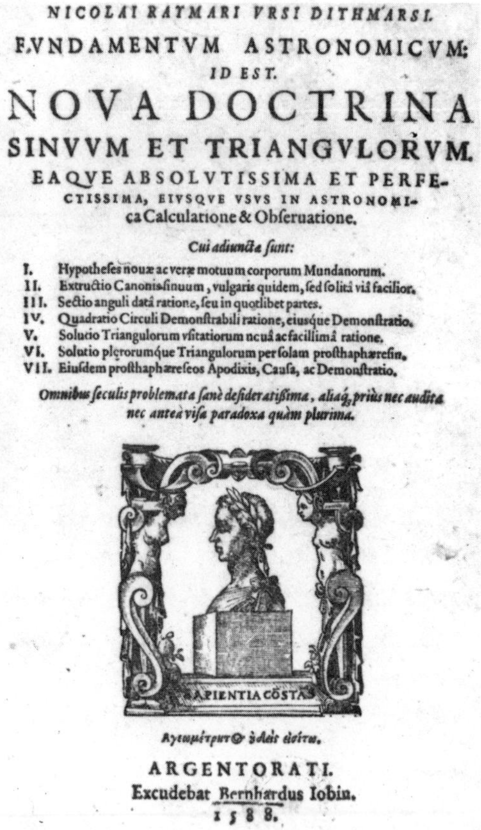
NICOLAI RAYMARI VRSI DITHMARSI.
FVNDAMENTVM ASTRONOMICVM:
ID EST.
NOVA DOCTRINA
SINVVM ET TRIANGVLORVM.
EAQVE ABSOLVTISSIMA ET PERFECTISSIMA, EIVSQVE VSVS IN ASTRONOMICA Calculatione & Obseruatione.

Cui adiuncta sunt:

I. Hypotheses nouæ ac veræ motuum corporum Mundanorum.
II. Extructio Canonis sinuum, vulgaris quidem, sed soliti via facilior.
III. Sectio anguli data ratione, seu in quotlibet partes.
IV. Quadratio Circuli Demonstrabili ratione, eiusque Demonstratio.
V. Solutio Triangulorum vsitatiorum ncua ac facillima ratione.
VI. Solutio plerorumque Triangulorum per solam prosthaphæresin.
VII. Eiusdem prosthaphæreseos Apodixis, Causa, ac Demonstratio.

Omnibus seculis problemata sanè desideratissima, aliaq. prius nec audita nec antea visa paradoxa quàm plurima.

SAPIENTIA CŌSTA

Ἀγεωμέτρητος οὐδεὶς εἰσίτω.

ARGENTORATI.
Excudebat Bernhardus Iobin.
1588.

9. Title Page of Nicholas Reimers Ursus, *Foundation of Astronomy*, Strasbourg, 1588

II

BRAHE'S DISCOVERY OF URSUS'S PLAGIARISM

II

BRAHE'S DISCOVERY OF URSUS'S PLAGIARISM

In September 1566 Brahe was forced to flee from Wittenberg because of the plague raging there. He betook himself instead to the University of
10 Rostock,□ where he became friendly with the professor of astronomy, Henry van den Brock (Brucaeus, 1530-1593). After leaving Rostock, where Brahe lost a piece of his nose in a duel, he corresponded with Brock. On 4 November 1588 he sent Brock a copy of his 13 September 1588 letter to Peucer:

> I am sending you a copy of the letter I recently wrote to the most illustrious and most learned Caspar Peucer, in which I thought I had to reply to certain doubts of his. (He communicated them to the most noble Heinrich Rantzau, who had sent him the straightforward exposition of the hypothesis excerpted from my book [*Stella caudata*]. I am also providing a copy of Peucer's remarks, together with the indecisive opinion of a certain other astronomer on the same subject.)[1]

This "certain other astronomer" is Brahe's Rullenhagen (Rollenhagen), who had already informed Rantzau

10. Rostock—a view from the North

(and thereby Brahe, too) about his conversation in 1586 concerning the cosmic hypotheses. As regards his letter of 4 November 1588, Brahe told Brock:

> When you have finished reading this letter, or even if you want to, have taken the trouble to have it copied, please send it back to me, since I want to keep this copy, and I don't have the facilities now to have it transcribed again.[2]

One of the reasons why Brahe wanted his letter returned was that it expressed his grievance about

> a certain excessively arrogant individual, whom I deem unworthy of being named here and who also, wherever he was or is, makes known what he is by shamelessly claiming for himself my invention of these hypotheses, and asserting this claim in a published book [*Foundation of Astronomy*], printed this year in Strasbourg. He may know whether he swiped this innovation together with the other things which he secretly copied in my establishment while he was serving the most noble man Eric Lange, in whose retinue he was present for several days, or by what method he otherwise removed that arrangement from here [Uraniburg]. My students pointed out that lying at that time among the discarded papers was something similar, which had been drawn less than accurately. How crookedly and craftily he acted here is certainly proved satisfactorily by the other things which he copied here without my knowledge. I recovered a part of them written with his own hand. Yet I do not find that hypothesis among those sheets. But he could have hidden it elsewhere or memorized it, when perhaps the opportunity for copying it was not available. The students in my establishment know that I devised this hypothesis and showed it to them several years ago. Indeed, although that book [*Stella caudata*] on the comet of the year

> [15]77 carries the imprint of this year [15]88, nevertheless all those who are with me know that it was printed on my press in the year [15]87, pains being taken to date it one year later to make it more acceptable on account of its recency. In this book, as you and I are not unaware on the basis of what has already been said, the same hypothesis is explained in general terms. But he who recently claimed it for himself makes it extraordinarily clear that he does not understand it properly, let alone that he is its author, by depicting and imagining Mars's sphere totally surrounding the sun's.[3]

In his *Foundation of Astronomy*, fol. 41, □ Ursus drew Mars's orbit completely enclosing the sun's, while at fol. 38r/#5 he talked about *11*

> Mars, the reddish planet, closest to the sun, located between the sun and Jupiter. These three planets [Saturn, Jupiter, Mars] encircle not only the sun, located almost at the center [of the universe], but also the earthly globe, which is sometimes closer to Mars, at other times farther away from it. When these planets are closest to the earth, they are said to be in perigee, but when they are farthest from it, they are said to be in apogee. The other two [Venus, Mercury], which follow in order, do not encircle the earth but the sun, just as the other three [Saturn, Jupiter, Mars] encircle the sun, which is located in the center of the universe.

Brahe often emphasized, as he did here in his letter to Brock, that Ursus deviated from the Tychonic system by depicting Mars's orbit surrounding the sun's, without intersecting it. This absence of intersection was Brahe's main weapon in his attack on Ursus for plagiarism. Had Brahe also been concerned to prove his plagiarist's incompetence, he could have pointed out that at fol. 38r/#5 Ursus described the sun as

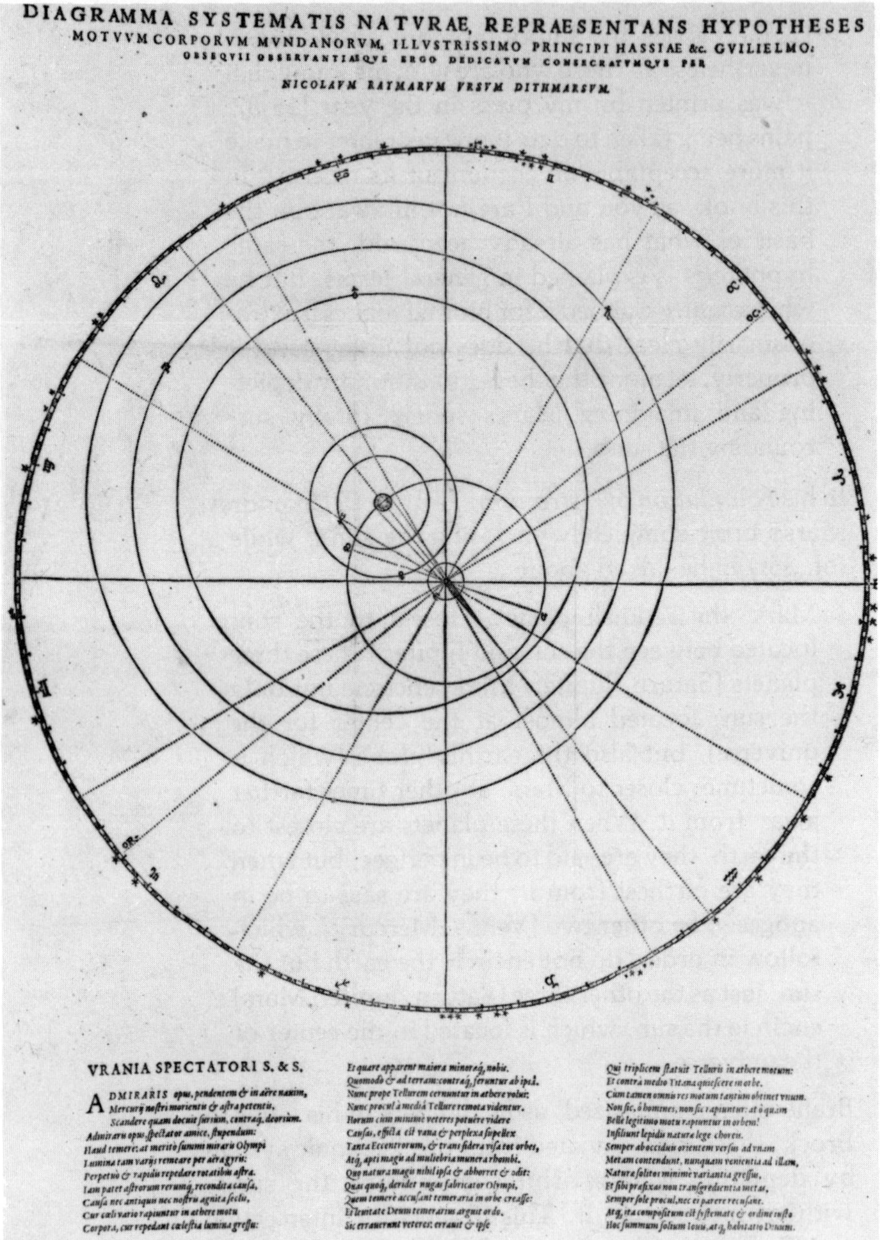

11. Ursus, *Foundation of Astronomy*, folio 41

"located almost at the center" (*in medio fere positum*) and "located in the center of the universe" (*in medio omnium situm*). These expressions echoed Copernicus,□ whose 12
sun was central on the universal scale and nearly central on the planetary scale.[4] On the larger scale Copernicus's sun was stationary;□ on the smaller scale, it might or 13
might not have a tiny correctional movement. On neither scale did it perform the annual revolution. This was performed, according to Ursus, by the sun far from the center of the universe (fol. 38r/XII, 1; fol. 41), while his sun also occupied that center (fol. 38r/5). Copernicus's "sun stationary in the middle of the world" was an error, according to Ursus's poem below the Diagram of the System of Nature (fol. 41/ right/2).

As regards Mars's orbit completely surrounding the sun's, in his letter of 4 November 1588 to Brock, Brahe contended that his plagiarist

> could have learned that this is impossible even from a merely superficial glance at Copernicus all by himself. And how, I ask, will he ever establish new hypotheses corresponding to the heavenly revolutions, since he has not mastered the precise observations of many years so as to elicit adroitly from them the defect in the hypotheses adopted heretofore, and the remedy capable of repairing that defect? Without these aids, bragging about a new discovery is pitiful and thoroughly ludicrous. For he lacks the means by which to prove from the phenomena why the earlier views must be abandoned and revised in this way, and how to establish by manifold observations that this innovation conforms more closely to the heavenly phenomena. These shortcomings, however, create a lack of confidence in them on the part of anybody, unless he fails to understand the subject.[5]

12. Copernicus, copper engraving after a portrait by a painter who may have known the astronomer as a middle-aged man

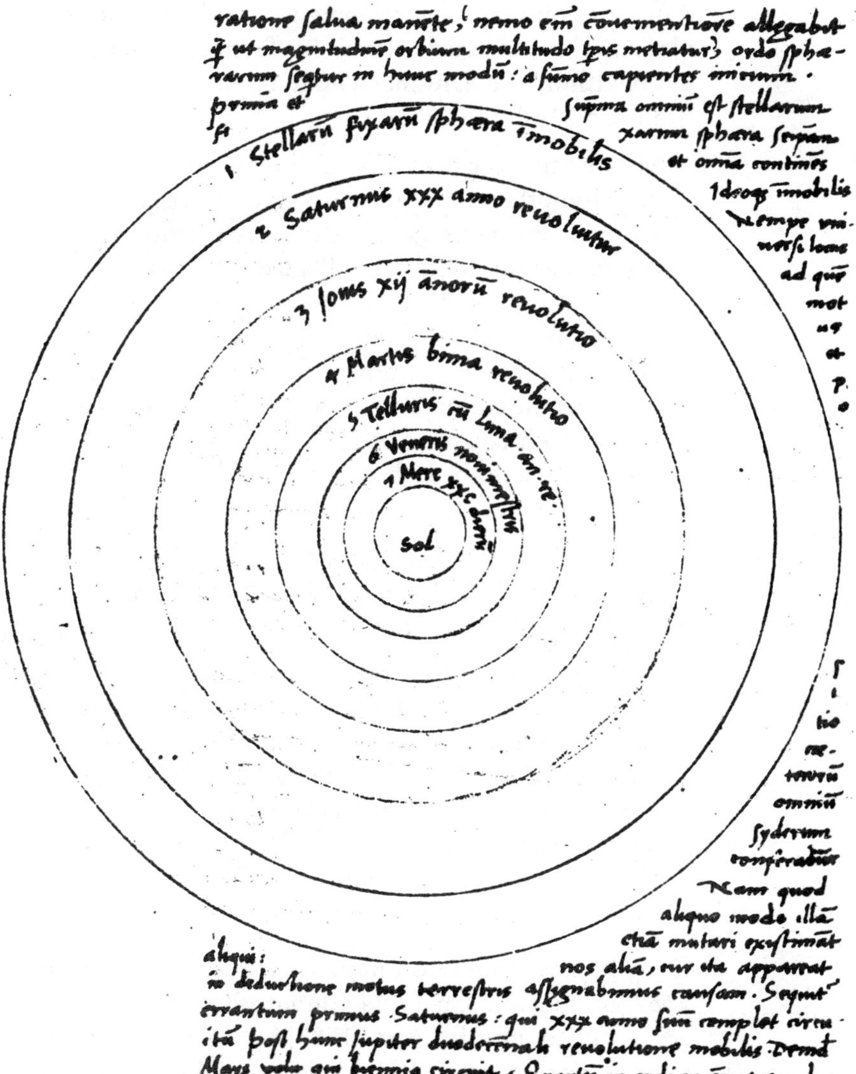

13. Copernicus's Cosmos, as drawn by himself

After listening to this vehement tirade against the plagiarist, Brock tried to calm his former pupil down by belittling the Dithmarschian in his response to Brahe on 23 March 1589:

> The fact that the man from Dithmarschen swiped your hypothesis is no reason for you to be greatly aroused. For since he lacks the observations by which the hypothesis is confirmed and the theory of the motions is constructed, he has gained nothing by adorning himself with the plumage of others, nor will he convince intelligent people that the innovation is his. Press forward with the work which you have begun, and prosecute your undertaking in the right spirit. This is the road to immortal glory.[6]

Meanwhile, on 21 December 1588, Brahe wrote to Rantzau about Ursus, who had deliberately adopted this Latin surname meaning "bear":

> In some letters which you sent me recently, you mentioned a certain Dithmarschian, who is like a bear in name and in fact. At the same time you transmitted an extract from a letter by the most renowned and most learned George Rollenhagen, together with that insolent plagiarist's book [*Foundation of Astronomy*, a copy of] which I had obtained previously elsewhere.[7]

In a letter written two months later, on 21 February 1589, Brahe said: "Ursus of Dithmarschen's book...had been sent to me...[in April 1588] by the very learned George Rollenhagen."[8] In his letter of 21 December 1588 to Rantzau, Brahe continued:

> Both you and Rollenhagen correctly suspect that the rearrangement of the hypotheses, which the Dithmarschian shamelessly attributed to himself, was swiped from me. That in fact is the case. True, he never worked for me or was part of my household, as you perhaps believe.[9]

In a letter to Rantzau, Rollenhagen had described Ursus as a former employee of Brahe.[10] In this letter of 21 December 1588, however, Brahe told Rantzau that Ursus had never been an employee of his, but had worked for a friend of his:

> Nevertheless four years ago the Dithmarschian was here [in Uraniburg] for about fourteen days with the most noble and most learned man Eric Lange of Engelsholm, who is well known to you, and for whom he was then working. While I was having a jolly good time with my close friend Eric and certain other nobles who were here with him, that crook secretly copied very many of the things I had researched with much labor and care. He sketched the design and arrangement of all the instruments which were then in service. He removed many other things which he could examine, nevertheless pretending he was doing none of these things, indeed he did not care for them but despised them. After I had smelled a whiff of his cunning, however, I arranged for someone else to recover a large part of what he had stolen, and I still have it. I see now that he sketched more than I recovered or even committed it to memory. For this rearrangement of the hypotheses never occurred to anybody before me, as far as I know. But from what I recently wrote to Peucer you will have an adequate understanding of how this discovery came about.[11]

In his letter to Rantzau of 13 September 1588 Brahe had enclosed a copy of his letter of the same date to Peucer in which he explained in full detail why he rejected the old cosmic hypotheses and devised his own.[12] In his letter to Rantzau of 21 December 1588 Brahe continued his account of what happened in Uraniburg in 1584:

> On the other hand, the Dithmarschian's theft of this hypothesis from me at that time is quite clearly deduced by me from the following considera-

tions. My friend Eric wanted me to account for the planets' varying appearances and retrograde motions. I gave him the explanation according to the ancient Ptolemaic as well as the Copernican thinking by drawing it on the table. I also added that the same results could be achieved by a certain other assumption, and I exposed certain absurdities in those earlier views. Eric (with his thoroughly open mind and thirst for knowledge) asked me to show him this arrangement, too. He noticed that I was reluctant to do so while that Dithmarschian servant of his was standing around and watching (for I had previously indicated to him that from the fellow's habits and appearance I had surmised what type he was). Sending him outside to do something else, Eric obtained from me what he wanted. I sketched for him my hypotheses, too, drawn in a general and brief manner, but I erased them right away.

But that Dithmarschian sensed that something secret was being discussed, as he was somewhat nosy. For that reason he investigated pretty carefully whether he could find something of this sort and take it away furtively. Thus among my papers lying on a window sill he came across a certain sketch of this arrangement of the heavenly motions which, however, through some negligence or other was drawn in such a way that Mars's sphere completely enveloped the sun's. This, being incorrect, was discarded and set aside as unsuitable and out of line. Yet he grabbed it as the true and correct sketch. Later on, either he drew it secretly or committed it to memory. Now, lying insolently, he advertises it as his own invention. He has pretended that he thought it out three years ago in a certain corner of the kingdom of Poland (where undoubtedly he never was). Without any shame he dedicates it to the most illustrious prince, the Landgrave, as though it were his own discovery.[13]

In his *Foundation of Astronomy* Ursus dedicated his Diagram of the System of Nature (fol. 41) to the Landgrave of Hesse, William IV□ (1532-1592). At fol. 37r/ 14
5-23 he introduced

> my new, not untrue, and natural hypotheses of the motions of the planets or heavenly bodies. I thought them out about three years ago in a certain remote corner of the very extensive kingdom of Poland. Afterwards I offered them to the most illustrious prince of Hesse,

whose technician constructed a bronze instrument to exhibit them mechanically. This instrument was lauded by Ursus as

> previously unheard of, absolutely unknown in all [previous] ages, and about to be disclosed to inspection by the whole world, to facilitate the observation and computation of all the motions of the heavenly bodies or movable components in the cosmic structure.

In his letter to Rantzau of 21 December 1588 Brahe continued his onslaught against Ursus:

> So vast is the disreputable impertinence of this man or rather bear. He copies the style of the erroneous drawing which he finds here and reproduces the same size [of Mars's orbit in comparison with the sun's] (for the sketch he saw here was erroneous, drawn on a whole unfolded sheet). He himself thereby sufficiently exposes his theft, and with indications that are not unclear he proclaims that he does not really understand the very things he brags about, much less that he originated and discovered them. In like manner very many of the other things, indeed the most important and nearly everything which he advertises in that book as his own, even though not all of it was derived from me, were nevertheless taken from other mathematicians, either with their knowledge or

14. William IV (1532-1592), Landgrave of Hesse, aged 45, painted in 1577, presumably by Caspar van der Borcht (+ 1610), appointed Hessian court painter in 1576

without it. Consequently, he does almost nothing else in that entire book than adorn himself with the feathers of others by attributing to himself with excessive arrogance the discoveries and results of others, and by promising what he never learned or can provide. But that despoiler is not worth my writing more about him, and perhaps this is too much. Nevertheless I could not refrain from pointing out to you how it happened that he got hold of my hypotheses and published them right away. Thus not only you but also Rollenhagen may know for a fact that his display of this hypothesis is pure theft. Indeed you are right in asserting that even though Ursus swiped my results, basically he still did not understand everything. This is clear from that mistaken drawing he presents, where he disgracefully does not know the size of Mars's sphere in relation to the sun's.

Rollenhagen also forthrightly and sagely points out that I should list what was removed from me by a runaway employee and taken away, so that it may be rightfully restored to the true inventor. For I understand he immediately recognized in Ursus's book that the innovation which he advertises as his own came from me, since he had previously written to you that this hypothesis had been communicated to him two years earlier by a runaway employee of mine. Yet I cannot quite infer from this whether he knows this Ursus, perhaps supposing that he once worked for me or is thinking of someone else who slipped away secretly from my establishment here. I therefore ask you, as soon as you have an opportunity to write to Rollenhagen, kindly to find out who that runaway employee of mine was and what his name was. Rollenhagen writes that he obtained the design of this hypothesis by way of this employee. For I would like to know whether he was Ursus or someone else. In fact, I know that none of my students who worked for me up to now in matters of astronomy left here secretly without my knowledge or permission. Nor can I quite figure out who that runaway was, mentioned by Rollenhagen more than once. Therefore if Rollenhagen identifies him for me, he will do me a very great favor.

I see that this Rollenhagen is not only a well-informed man, very impressive in his sound judgment, but also irreproachable, honest, and favorably disposed toward the researches of others. Accordingly, when the opportunity occurs, I shall not hesitate to initiate a friendly correspondence with him. But if he makes the first move, that in itself will provide a satisfactory opportunity.

This letter, however, is longer than I intended. Yours will be the task of honestly interpreting this waste of time, caused by a just complaint.

If you receive a letter from Dr. Peucer addressed to me, I ask you not to find it any trouble to send it here right away. Farewell, most noble and most distinguished sir. Do not fail to serve scholarly pursuits, as you do, and in this way gain imperishable fame. Once more, live and be well in complete happiness and for a very long time.

Written in Uraniburg, 21 December 1588[14]

III

THE LANDGRAVE'S PLANETARIUM

III

THE LANDGRAVE'S PLANETARIUM

The specialists to whom Brahe sent copies of his *Stella caudata* included the Hessian Landgrave's mathematician, Christopher Rothmann,[1] whose honest reaction was later requested by Brahe in a letter dated 17 August 1588:

> I suppose that in the meantime you have also read that book carefully, so that you may accordingly inform me of your opinion of what it contains. I am most eager for you to set forth your thinking about these matters sincerely.[2]

Later in this lengthy letter, after rejecting the traditional and recent astronomical systems, Brahe disclosed to Rothmann his plan to develop his hypothesis in a forthcoming publication:

> I shall endeavor to fit my corrections in the movements of all the planets to my own hypotheses, which I devised not so long ago. I have decided to show the agreement of the computations with these corrections and to that extent with heaven itself, and to expound the agreement in a special work, by the favor of divine grace. However, you have a rather general sketch of this hypothesis in my *Recent Phenomena*

> *in the Celestial World, Book II,* which I have already sent you. The more carefully you examine this sketch, the more it will please you. For it gets rid of all the mathematical and physical absurdities lurking in the ancient Ptolemaic and modern Copernican theories, and it most neatly and completely satisfies the more specialized phenomena, a result that neither of the others provides in every detail, as I shall show from the observations themselves.[3]

Rothmann answered Brahe on 19 September 1588 in his characteristically dogged manner:

> I do not agree in all respects with your new hypotheses, mentioned in Chapter VIII [of *Stella caudata*],

and then went on to talk about the Landgrave's planetarium:

> Last year [1587] my most illustrious lord [the Landgrave of Hesse] ordered the construction of a machine, astonishingly small yet displaying the motions of all the planets...
> I cannot be absolutely certain whether your hypotheses are the same as these and agree with them.[4]

The Landgrave's planetarium puzzled Brahe until he received a copy of Ursus's *Foundation of Astronomy,* as he told Rothmann in his reply, dated 21 February 1589:

> At first I was greatly surprised when I read in your letter [of 19 September 1588] that the most illustrious lord [the Landgrave of Hesse] was previously familiar with these hypotheses of mine, having had a certain machine display them. I could not quite figure out how that could happen, since I knew very well that I had learned them from no mortal man before I myself was led to them by the observations, and meanwhile they were concealed in my papers and were not

> previously published. Later on, however, the little book [*Foundation of Astronomy*] by Ursus of Dithmarschen...was sent to me (by the very learned man George Rollenhagen, residing in Magdeburg, who also had previously informed me that these hypotheses of mine had been imparted to him two years earlier by a certain runaway employee of mine.[5]

Rollenhagen's report of his conversation about the hypotheses in 1586 reached Brahe through Rantzau as intermediary. In the same indirect way Rollenhagen sent a copy of Ursus's *Foundation of Astronomy* to Rantzau for Brahe, who received it in October, or perhaps November, 1588. Brahe's letter of 21 February 1589 to Rothmann continued:

> Rollenhagen, therefore, knowing that the hypotheses had been originated by me, and grieving that Ursus undeservedly claimed them for himself, wanted me to become familiar with that book in order to recognize that theft, and once more claim for myself what had been carried off by others). From this book I saw quite clearly whence this arrangement of the heavenly bodies came to you. For this plagiarist states that about three years earlier, after he had thought it out in a certain region of the kingdom of Poland (better interpret this as the island Hven in the kingdom of Denmark, when he was here in the year [15]84 in September with my close friend, the most noble and most learned Eric Lange, by whom he was then employed, and in my house secretly stole these hypotheses, like certain other materials), he proposed it to the most illustrious Landgrave of Hesse, and it was rendered as a bronze machine
> 15 by Jost Bürgi, □ the Landgrave's technician.
>
> But this impostor betrays his theft clearly enough, and at the same time his ignorance of the merchandise he peddles. For in drawing Mars's

15. Jost Bürgi (1552-1632), William IV's technician; at the age of 67, his portrait was drawn on 28 February 1619 by Egidius Sadeler (1570-1629), court painter of the emperors Rudolph II and Matthias

orbit completely enclosing the sun's, he copies a certain incorrect diagram which had been drawn in this way through some inadvertence and for that reason was thrown away somewhere among my papers as inaccurate. I still have it in my hands, because it was tracked down to make this matter absolutely clear. Since he could not correct the error committed in the drawing of the diagram, he makes it known to those with sufficient understanding that he does not comprehend this innovation, much less is its author, although he unashamedly claimed it arrogantly as his own research and dedicated it to the most illustrious Landgrave William as his own invention. Besides, he has many other matters in that little book of his which, although he did not steal them all from here, he nevertheless scraped together partly from you, partly from other astronomers in Germany, either covertly or overtly, so that if the material belonging to others is removed, practically nothing remains which is his own. But he persists in his plagiarism, while to you and other scholars, with whom he once tarried, it is quite clear who he is, and what an arrogant and scheming trifler he is.[6] This is what I wanted to say briefly about my hypotheses. In a better place and time you will find out more, which will undoubtedly satisfy you (unless you have committed yourself very strictly to Copernicus's language and theory).[7]

IV

URSUS IN STRASBOURG

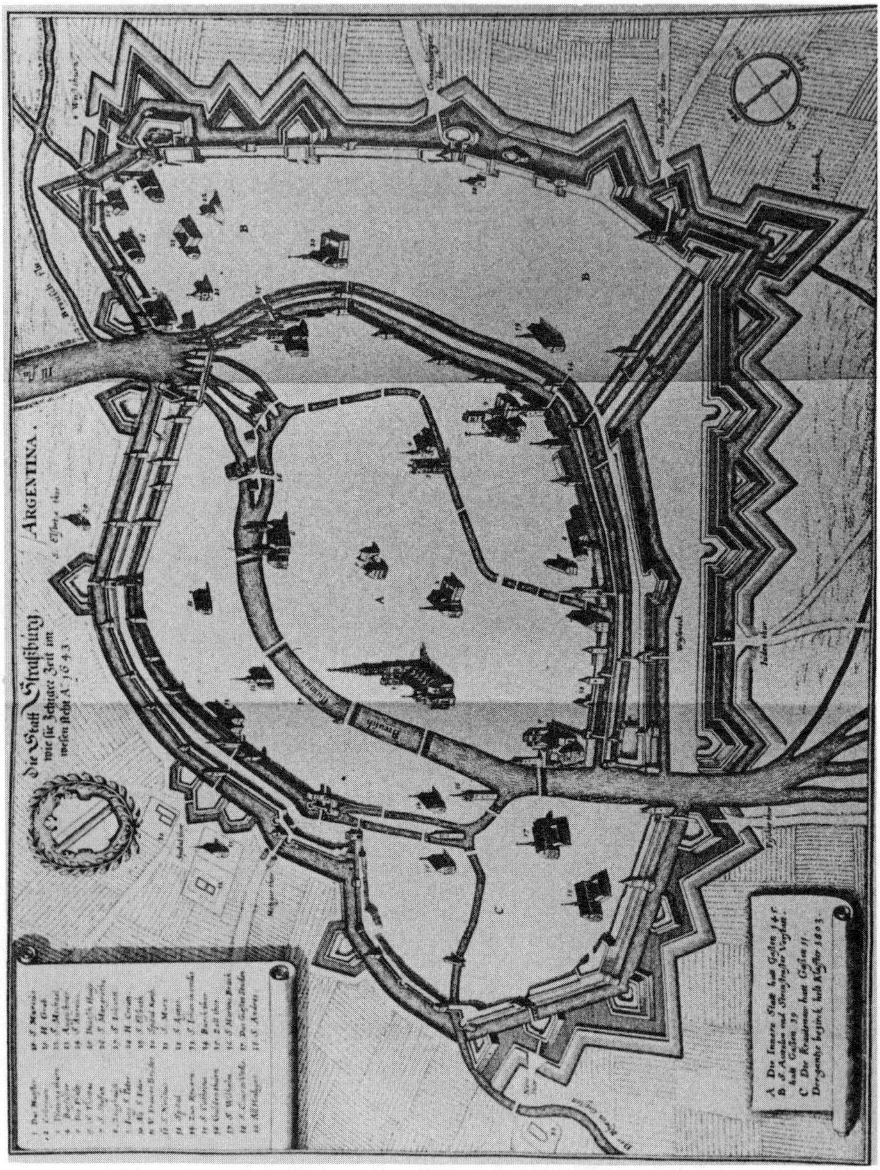

16. Strasbourg, in 1643

IV

URSUS IN STRASBOURG

In dedicating his *Foundation of Astronomy* to the
three administrators of Strasbourg Academy on 31 July
1588, Ursus said he had come to visit the city□ and the 16
Academy "a year earlier."[1] He named a number of
distinguished men he had met there, but kept quiet
about Helisaeus Roeslin (1548-1616), a physician and
cosmologist. On 9 April 1588 Roeslin wrote to Michael
Maestlin□ (1550-1631), professor of astronomy at the 17
University of Tübingen:□ 18

> There is in Strasbourg an astronomy student who is now of advanced age [Ursus was then thirty-seven, twice as old as the average student]. In addition, he gives private instruction, especially in trigonometry, which he claims he has mastered, and also plans to publish. Coming from Holstein, he tells me, he also visited Tycho Brahe, worked for him, and helped him in his astronomical observations and calculations. But he does not think so highly of him, and also does not believe he will fulfill his promises. Yet Brahe pretends that with the help of thirty-six circles he will explain all the astronomical phenomena. But this Holsteiner does not agree that anything will come of this. He says Tycho is more of an astrologer than an astronomer, his basis being in particular

17. Michael Maestlin (1550-1631), Kepler's professor of astronomy at the University of Tübingen; painted in 1619

18. Tübingen, where Kepler studied astronomy under Maestlin

> Ptolemy's basis. On the other hand, this Holsteiner has a different basis. I don't know his name.[2]

A month and a half after Ursus's *Foundation of Astronomy* was published, Roeslin wrote again to Maestlin on 15 September 1588:

> I assume you have received that Holsteiner's publication from the author himself. Please write me your opinion of his earlier chapters [Ch. I-III concern mathematics], since I do not deal with them but, as far as I understand, they are on the whole absolutely correct and demonstrated. I comprehend his last chapter [Ch. V: The Observation of the Motions of the Planets, including my New Hypotheses] on the system of the world quite well, but he slips into many absurdities. Hence he would have done well to stay with Copernicus's hypotheses until he found better ones, especially because his hypotheses advance astronomical computations no further than Copernicus's hypotheses. He would be better off had he eliminated the last chapter. He would have exerted himself a great deal and worked for nothing, and yet might not be certain whether he had already thereby acquired the Landgrave [of Hesse] as his patron.[3]

On the title page of his *Chronotheatrum* (Prague, 1597) Ursus explained that this work had been "sketched out in Hesse in 1586."[4] Two years later, however, in talking to Roeslin before the *Foundation of Astronomy* was published, Ursus had deemed it prudent to
19 avoid mentioning that he had been in Kassel□ with the Landgrave, had antagonized Rothmann, and had left without a recommendation. Nevertheless, by dedicating to the Landgrave the Diagram of the System of Nature, the culmination of his *Foundation of Astronomy*, Ursus was implicitly appealing to the Landgrave to take him back. Maestlin must have answered Roeslin's letter quite promptly, since Roeslin's reply was dated 28 October 1588:

19. Kassel, site of William IV's observatory

must have answered Roeslin's letter quite promptly, since Roeslin's reply was dated 28 October 1588:

> As far as I understand from your letter, the opinion of both Tycho and Reimers is virtually one and the same with regard to the system of the world, and the hypotheses of both are almost identical. Indeed, Reimers admitted to me that he had been Tycho's pupil, or rather that Tycho had made use of his work in observing and calculating the planetary motions. But he said Tycho had a different point of view and came quite close to Ptolemy's hypotheses. He also added that professionally Tycho is not the man many think him to be, being an astrologer rather than an astronomer, and will not accomplish what many expect of him. Yet as far as I gather from your letter, he has certainly accomplished something. Thus one is jealous of the other, conduct unbecoming a pupil.[5]

Perhaps without receiving any response from Maestlin, Roeslin wrote to him again on 15 December 1588:

> As far as the system of the world is concerned, I find that Reimers has his from Tycho, and made the earth movable lest he appear to be in agreement with Tycho [for whom the earth was immovable]. Neither Tycho's system nor Reimers's completely satisfies me. I categorically declare that the planets are moved on fixed spheres. I even prove this on the basis of Tycho in the following way. He attributes to each of the planets its own motion. Then, since for him the earth does not move, he must ascribe to all the planets also the motion engendered by the First Movable [the outermost sphere of the stars regarded as undergoing a daily rotation, transmitted to the planets]. And if the completely individual motion of the planets could be caused

> by their own implanted consciousness and not by spheres, how could the annual motion be a property of the planets if they were not attached to spheres? I categorically maintain that there are real spheres in the aether. If this does not fit the comets exactly, I defend this position in the very same way as must be done also in Tycho's way. He apparently wants to put the comet of the year 1580 beyond the firmament of the fixed stars. Then it would truly rush onward mightily. Moreover, Tycho does not understand Genesis, Chapter I; neither does Reimers. I conclude that a different system of the world can be elicited from that chapter.
>
> My theses concerning the system of the world, which I opposed to Reimers's theses, I sent to my kinsman in Heimerdingen.[6] In due course he will send them to you. You will learn my point of view which, however, I do not hold obstinately. I want to be instructed. Surely Copernicus acts in opposition to the principles of physics and in opposition to Holy Scripture. I am not an astronomer. I only want to be able in a general way to know how creation proceeded in the world and in the spheres. Therefore I accept detailed information from the specialists.[7]

Nearly nine years later Roeslin showed his *De opere Dei creationis seu de mundo hypotheses* (The Work of God the Creator, or Hypotheses Concerning the World) to the scholarly diplomat Jacques Bongars☐ 20
(1554-1612):

> He took it with him to Frankfurt and had it printed in [15]97. At that time I was not completely decided about this investigation of Nature.[8]

On account of this uncertainty, Roeslin later recalled, when his *Work of God the Creator* was already partly finished, in order to obtain Maestlin's opinion of it, I sent it to him in Tübingen in a package, together with a letter attached to the top of it, in which there was an explanation of the system I had discovered. On the way, however, this package came into the hands of my good friend, a scholar,[9] to whom I had written about it. He opens the package, and keeps it with my system, to think these things over. But he lets the letter go on to Maestlin, who supposed that I was writing to him about Reimers's system. For that reason he replies to me about it and not about my own. But at the same time he also sent me Tycho's printed publication about the comet of

20. Jacques Bongars (1554-1612), French diplomat and scholar

1577, in which he too mentions his own system. Thus I discovered that Tycho's system and mine were like one.

When I later published these theses of mine ten years ago [Roeslin is writing in 1607 in Chapter III, On Astronomical Hypotheses, of his *Historischer, Politischer und Astronomischer natürlicher Discurs* (Strasbourg, 1609)] and announced how my thoughts about the system of the world came to me, Ursus, at that time the Mathematician at the Imperial Court, lets loose a defamatory publication against Tycho, Rothmann, and Roeslin all together, and accuses me of having everything from Tycho, and even having stolen it from him, and now pretending that it is my own. But the letters, mentioned previously [in the *Discurs*], and their date prove that the opposite is true, and that Ursus treated me outrageously and wrongfully. But he himself impelled me onward and at the same time he indirectly became my instructor in these matters, not Tycho. If any theft occurred in this affair, it originated with him when he left Tycho and broke with him. For this reason, then, Tycho publicly in print denounced him as a foul creature and a scoundrel on account of the aforementioned defamatory publication. But afterwards he did not answer the defamation. Neither did I, disregarding the written warning of Kepler, then in Styria, that I should take a stand against this Ursus the Bear and upset him. But I did not do this, deeming him unworthy of an answer. For every intelligent scholar can judge and refute such a publication and defamation, and make a distinction between him and me. Besides, he soon thereafter got his reward in the form of a timely death.

At the imperial court his successor and follower [after Brahe][10] was Kepler, still a young man with an exceptionally brilliant mind and in-

> telligence, known to me for many years through private correspondence.[11] I consider him worthy of being an interlocutor not only where we agree but also where I believe that he wronged me in writing or that he himself has gone astray. I would defend myself, and rebut and rebuke him, not with calumnies and curses (as is now the custom of perverse scholars) but as befits Christians in their mutual relations, with friendliness and instruction. I want to be and remain his friend, even if we are already in disagreement about several matters.[12]

To defend himself againt Ursus's accusation that he had plagiarized Brahe, Roeslin declared in Chapter III of his *Discurs*:

> Tycho Brahe's new basis for the system of the world pleases me more than Ptolemy's ancient basis and Copernicus's new basis, because it harmonizes best with Holy Scripture and physics, and because it entered my mind and thinking before it came to me from elsewhere. Thus, while I always doubted the Copernican basis but could not extricate myself from it, Reimers Ursus, who had previously been with Tycho Brahe in Denmark, happened to come to Strasbourg with a new system which, however, he took from Tycho's system and changed it only so that he would produce something special and submerge his teacher's doctrines. But because this system had many more and cruder absurdities and inanities than Copernicus, I could approve of it even less. But I thought about the matter diligently, and spun the circle of the planets around, until I finally arrived at Tycho's thinking and his system, from which Reimers took his.[13]

Not only did Roeslin publicly accuse Ursus of taking his system from Brahe's, but he also declared in a private letter that in Strasbourg he had let Ursus read

an unpublished manuscript only to find some of its conceptions repeated without acknowledgment in Ursus's *Chronotheatrum*.[14] This charge of plagiarism against Ursus was contained in a letter sent on 4/14 May 1597 by Roeslin to Hans Georg Herwart of Hohenburg□ (1553-1622), chancellor of the duchy of 21
Bavaria.[15]

21. Joannes Georg Herwart von Hohenburg (1553-1622), aged 69, chancellor of the duchy of Bavaria and patron of Kepler

Roeslin's denunciation of Ursus's *Foundation of Astronomy* for stealing Tycho's system was published in 1609, long after the death of Ursus, who may never have known that Roeslin also accused him privately of committing plagiarism in his *Chronotheatrum*. That work was likewise assailed, not only by Roeslin in faraway Alsace, but right in Prague itself, where Ursus felt the full force of the blows and fought back:

22 Certain foreigners, running around Prague, □ jealous of me as a German in outlook and descent, most falsely and untruthfully spread rumors about me to the effect that I copied everything in my *Chronotheatrum*, printed this year [1597], word for word, down to the very title, from a published open letter, written by an Englishman, Alan Cope.[16] But I solemnly swear that I did not see that letter, nor do I believe that it exists. If perchance anybody has seen it, I beg him to notify me so that it may be compared with my *Chronotheatrum*.[17]

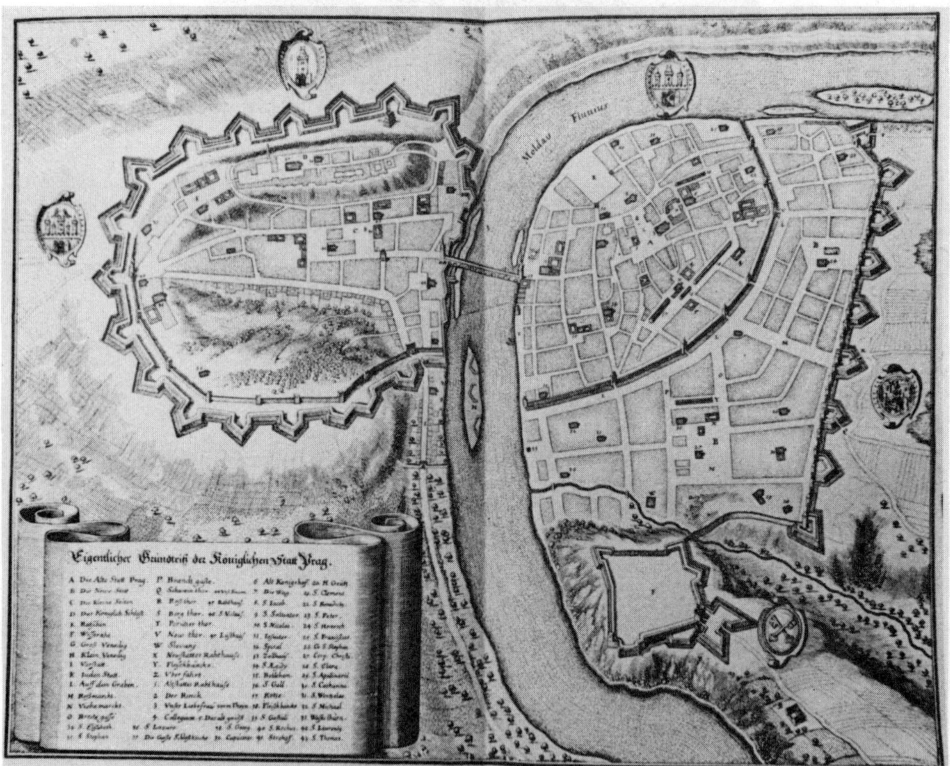

22. Prague, capital of the Holy Roman Empire under Rudolph II

V

URSUS'S APPOINTMENT AS IMPERIAL MATHEMATICIAN

V

URSUS'S APPOINTMENT AS IMPERIAL MATHEMATICIAN

In his *Foundation of Astronomy* Ursus acknowledged that he was destitute. In his frantic search for some remunerative employment, he resorted to the unusual device of dedicating each of twenty-one diagrams in his *Foundation of Astronomy* to a potential sponsor. In this way he publicly appealed (fol. 7r) to Konrad Dasypodius, Jr., a son of his teacher at Strasbourg. Konrad Dasypodius, Sr., used a latinized form of his family's German surname. So had his father Peter, who in his influential Latin-German dictionary equated *dasypus* with *Haas* (German for "hare"). Peter Dasypodius's equation (*dasypus* = *Haas*) suggested that the German surname might have been related somehow to *Haas*.[1] *Rauhfuss*, by contrast, had previously been put forward arbitrarily.[2] *Rauchfuss* was also proposed.[3] So was *Hasenfratz* or *Hasenfuss*.[4]

Just as Dasypodius's former German surname is not certified by any document, so the exact dates of his birth and death are obscured. He is said to have died "in his 68th year."[5] But he wrote to Kepler that he was already "at this advanced age of 70 years."[6] As a prolific author of mathematical treatises, Dasypodius thereby indicated that on 31 December 1599 he had already completed his 70th year. Hence he was born in 1529. The date of his death is less certain. It has been placed in April, 1600[7] or 1601.[8] In 1604 a letter was written to Kepler by a correspondent who discussed his late mentor Dasypodius. Somehow Kepler received the mistaken impression that Dasypodius died in 1604.[9]

This correspondent also told Kepler that in Strasbourg in 1599 Dasypodius had published a broadside listing his own writings and his translations, printed or projected, of various Greek authors into Latin:[10]

> In Dasypodius's library I saw all the books listed there which he had caused to be copied, while he was in France, at great expense in the royal
> library established by Francis I.☐ He also had 23
> certain other books, already printed, namely, mathematical works of Archimedes, Commandino, and certain [other] Italians. But even though I have searched carefully, I have not yet been able to find out where all those things went. For that fine old man was quite unhappy on account of his wife and children, who brought him terrible trouble and impeded his serious projects. For of the four wives whom he had married, the first and the last, who is still alive, were very well behaved and most attentive to family matters. But of the third one, who suffered from a certain incurable disease, he dissolved the marriage after the third month. The second one, however, who was too extravagant, in a short time contracted a huge debt, which he was compelled to pay after her death and at the same time to repay to her relatives her dowry as a wife who died childless. Hence almost all his property would have been dissipated had not the post of ecclesiastical dean [in the Chapter of St. Thomas in Strasbourg], which he held at that time together with his professorship of mathematics, supported his family structure, which was about to collapse.

23. Francis I, king of France from 1515 to 1547; drawn by François Clouet (c. 1522-1572)

As far as his children are concerned, of his
two sons, who were about to enter the age of
manhood, he tearfully attended the funeral
processions, which occurred within an interval of a few months. One of them had suffered more than fifteen years and had pitifully
been released from his body, whereas the
other was already married and had recently
gladdened him with a grandchild. Two
daughters are left. One of them, made pregnant by a certain noble friend of his, afterwards married a certain private scribe and
was taken away to Meissen. The other, who
still lives in Strasbourg, chose a certain craftsman as her husband. When he unhappily
entered into a contract, defrauded by his
associate, he was deprived of almost all his
goods. As I recently learned, almost all his
furniture was auctioned off, and I believe that
Dasypodius's books, which had descended to
him by heredity, also were on the block,
especially since Dasypodius, while still alive,
acting as a guarantor, had pledged his credit
for his son-in-law. Dasypodius had foreseen
all this, and therefore, as he frequently mentioned to me, he had decided to bequeath his
manuscripts to the Illustrious Maurice, Landgrave of Hesse, □ so that they would be add- 24
ed to the Landgrave's library. It is not yet
clear to me what happened after Dasypodius's
death. Within a short time, however, I expect
an answer from a certain friend who, I trust,
will explain the particular circumstances to
me. It undoubtedly seems that by a secret
power of fate those who carefully pursue
these excellent studies, removed from the
understanding of ordinary people, find it
necessary to contend with many sorrows and
misfortunes which either delay or completely

24. Maurice, Landgrave of Hesse (1572-1632), aged 44, drawn and engraved in 1616 by Crispin van de Passe (c. 1565-1637)

block their efforts, worthy of praise and immortal fame.[11]

In his *Foundation of Astronomy* Ursus dedicated a
diagram also to Bürgi, his former teacher at Kassel.[12]
Then he turned to Simon Duchesne, who called himself
"van der Eycke" after he fled from France to avoid
religious persecution. His Dutch treatise on the squaring
of the circle (*Claerder bewys op de quadrature des
cirkels*, Delft, 1586), was translated into Latin and
German by Ursus.[13] His table companion at Strasbourg
was David Wolkenstein, the professor of mathematics
there.[14] Ursus, who was born in Dithmarschen, called
Thomas Finck, a native of Flensburg in Schleswig, his
"fellow-countryman."[15] Finck had edited Rantzau's
Horoscopographia. At Kassel, Ursus had known Paul
Wittich.[16] Bartholomew Scultetus□ (Schultz) had 25
written on the calendar and other astronomical topics.[17]
The eminent mathematical geographers, Gerard
Mercator,□ his sons (Rumold and Arnold), and 26
grandson (Arnold's son, Johannes) also received a
dedication.[18] So did Edo Hilderic□ of Friesland.[19] Peter 27
Apian's son, Philip,□ had invented a new mathemati- 28
cal instrument.[20] Maestlin, Kepler's professor of
astronomy at the University of Tübingen, was not
overlooked.[21] Rheticus's disciple, Valentin Otho, was
included.[22] Ursus may not have known that Brock, the
professor of astronomy at the University of Rostock,
was a friend and correspondent of Brahe.[23] Christopher
Clavius,□ the famous commentator on Sacrobosco, 29
received a dedication.[24] Johannes Junge, of Schweid-
nitz□ in Silesia, around 1577 had devised a method of 30
finding the rational, integral roots of numerical
equations of higher degree.[25] In his posthumous
Arithmetica analytica, vulgo Cosa, oder Algebra
(Frankfurt on the Oder, 1601), Ursus claimed he had
improved Junge's method.[26] Another of Ursus's
dedicatees was Victor Schönfeld□ of Bautzen, an 31

25. Bartholomew Scultetus (1532-1614), friend of Tycho Brahe; woodcut by Jürgen Scharfemberch in 1572

26. Gerard Mercator (1512-1594), cartographer, aged 64; copper engraving executed in 1576 by Hendrik Goltzius (1558-1617)

D. EDO HILDERICVS à Varel
Nobilis Friso
Primo Mathemat. A° 1564. Jenens. tum
Francof. ad Viadr. A° 1575. Hist. et Hebr L. hinc
S. Theol. Heidelb. A° 1578. ac denique Ejusdem
Theolog. Prof. Primarius A° 1580 Altorphinus.
Nat. d. A° 1533. Den. d. 19. Maji A° 1599.
W. P. K. fc.

27. Edo Hilderic of Friesland (1533-1599); engraving by Wolfgang Philipp Kilian (1654-1732) from his own sketch

28. Philip Apian (1531-1589), professor of astronomy at the University of Tübingen, where he was succeeded by Maestlin

29. Christopher Clavius (1537-1612), principal proponent of the Gregorian calendar

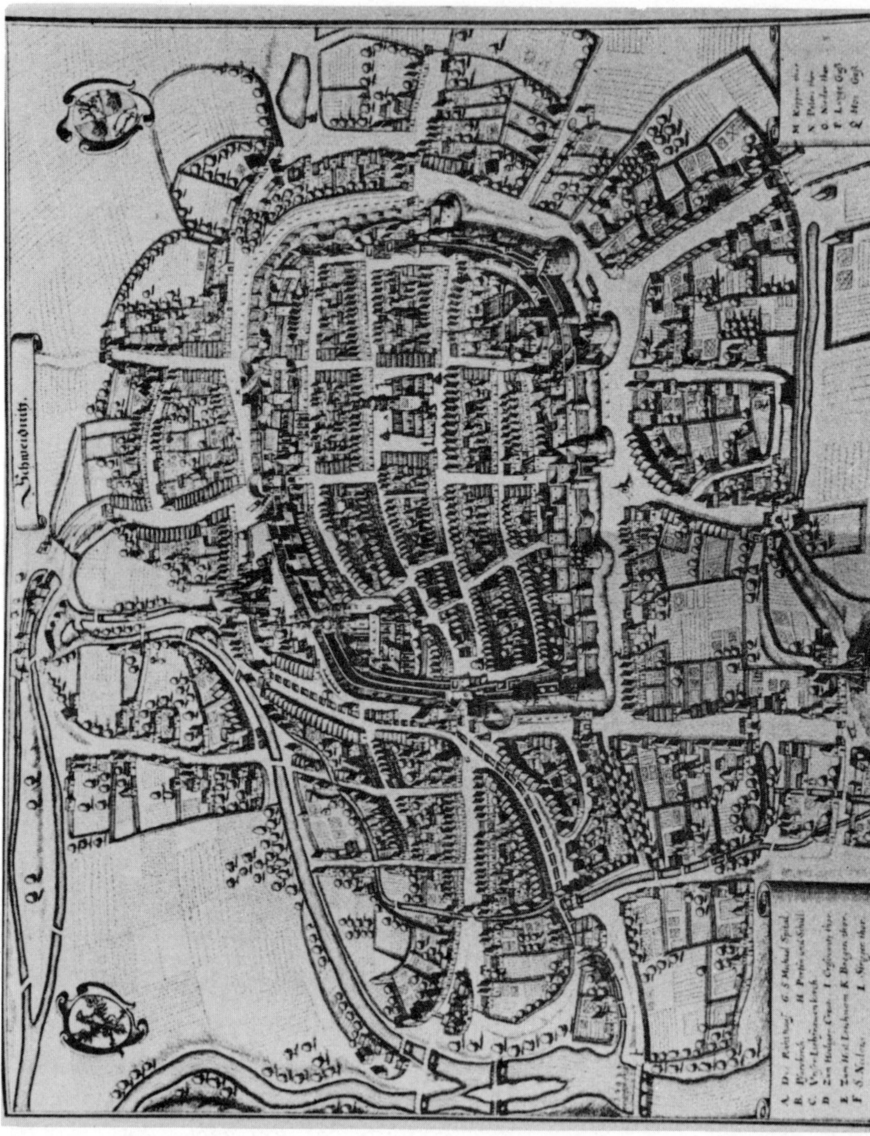

30. Schweidnitz, birthplace of Johannes Junge, who introduced a method of finding the rational roots of a numerical equation

31. Victor Schönfeld (1525-1591), professor of mathematics and medicine at the University of Marburg

astrologer and medical writer.[27] So was Peucer, also of Bautzen, professor of astronomy at the University of Wittenberg.[28] Ursus even looked abroad to John Dee, □ 32
author of the renowned introduction to the first English translation of Euclid.[29] Ursus also looked back to the Landgrave of Hesse, who was tutored in mathematics by Rumold Mercator, and for whom maps were made by Arnold Mercator and his son Johannes.[30] Ursus directed his main effort to Strasbourg by dedicating the entire book, *Foundation of Astronomy*, to the three superintendents of the local Academy, John Philip Kettenheim, Abraham Heltius, and Nicholas Hugo Kniebs. The local professor of law, Lawrence Tuppius of Pomerania, was not overlooked.[31]

Ursus did not succeed in establishing himself at Strasbourg, and tried his luck in Frankfurt am Main.

32. John Dee (1527-1608) signed Christopher Rothmann's friendship album in Kassel on 26 March 1589; a portrait of Dee, aged 67, in the Ashmolean Museum, Oxford, was copied by Silvester Harding (1745-1809) and engraved by Scheneker

33. Thaddeus Háyek (1525-1600), friend of Tycho Brahe; portrait drawn by Jan Jakub Quirin Jahn (1739-1802) and engraved by Jan Balzer (1738-1799) in Prague

He had dedicated a diagram (fol. 28r) in his *Foundation of Astronomy* to Matthew Bader, the rector of the local school. While in Frankfurt, Ursus received the exhilarating news that he had been appointed Imperial Mathematician. Rudolph II had accepted the recommendation of his Vice-Chancellor, Jacob Kurtz. From Prague, the imperial capital, on 19/29 August
33 1591 the physician Thaddeus Háyek□ (1525-1600) wrote to his friend Brahe that

> Nicholas Reimers, whom you had accused of plagiarism, came here several weeks ago and notified Kurtz, who had recommended him to the emperor for this post, that he had been appointed [Imperial] Mathematician, at quite a low salary at the start. Today he left for Frankfurt to move his belongings, and will return here soon.[32]

VI

THE KEPLER-URSUS CORRESPONDENCE

34. Johannes Kepler (1571-1630), Imperial Mathematician from 1601-1630

VI

THE KEPLER-URSUS CORRESPONDENCE

Johannes Kepler□ (1571-1630) was hard at work 34
preparing his first major publication for the press while
he was still a relatively unknown teacher of
mathematics in the Austrian town of Graz.□ One of 35
his supervisors was a young nobleman named Hans
Sigismund Wagn□ of Wagensberg, who used to make 36
frequent trips to Prague, then the capital of the Holy Roman Empire. There Wagn met the Imperial Mathematician, Ursus, whom he greatly admired. Wagn told Kepler that Ursus was a remarkably gifted man, well known by reputation throughout Germany and Italy. He encouraged Kepler to feel no hesitation in using his name while getting in touch with Ursus. As a result, on one of his journeys from Graz to Prague, Wagn carried a letter written by Kepler to Ursus, which began with the self-justifying observation that

> People who send messages to strangers in faraway places are peculiar. You were made known to me long ago by your most illustrious glory, in which you alone outstrip the astronomers of this age as much as Phoebus's orb [outshines] the tiny stars. Time, however, does not permit more [compliments], nor is long-

35. Graz, capital of the Austrian province of Styria; on stylistic grounds the engraving may be attributed to Matthaeus Merian Sr. (1593-1650)

36. Hans Sigismund Wagn of Wagensberg, a supervisor of Kepler in Graz

> windedness becoming to astronomers. Of this one thing be sure, that I think as much of you as do all scholars. To despise their judgment is a mark of impertinence, to join their praise befits a modest youth. Accordingly, since the little knowledge I have in astronomy I acquired with you, that is, with your books, as my teacher, I thought it right to consult you in a matter that is difficult and, in my opinion, not trivial. If you approve of what I say, I shall consider myself fortunate. To be corrected by you, I regard as the highest stage of happiness, so much do I value your judgment. I love your hypotheses. But I cannot admire Copernicus enough, whose hypotheses have a quality which I have caught in the following verses.[1]

Kepler then proceeded to quote the first six lines of a ten-line poem[2] which he had composed for the verso of the title page of his forthcoming book. In it he interdigitated the five regular solids of ancient Greek geometry with the six planetary orbits of the Copernican astronomy. Summarizing his results compactly in a few lines of prose, Kepler concluded his first letter to Ursus:

> I say no more while awaiting your judgment, which you will have no trouble in sending me on this or the next visit, thanks to the most noble young man Sigismund Wagn, at whose instance I am writing. Take care of yourself, for the sake of the stars and our science, O pride of Germany![3]

After dating this letter from Graz on 15 November 1595,[4] young Kepler committed the last of his many indiscretions therein by signing himself "Your Excellency's pupil."[5]

No matter how Kepler signed his letter, and no matter how (insincerely) flattering it was, Ursus did not reply, nor was he moved by what he heard from Wagn about Kepler. Ursus's contemptuous indifference

Prodromus

DISSERTATIONVM COSMOGRA-
PHICARVM, CONTINENS MYSTE-
RIVM COSMOGRAPHI-
CVM,

DE ADMIRABILI

PROPORTIONE ORBIVM
COELESTIVM, DEQVE CAVSIS
cœlorum numeri, magnitudinis, motuúmque periodicorum genuinis & pro-
prijs,

DEMONSTRATVM, PER QVINQVE
regularia corpora Geometrica,

A

M. IOANNE KEPLERO, VVIRTEM-
bergico, Illustrium Styriæ prouincia-
lium Mathematico.

Quotidiè morior, fateorque: sed inter Olympi
Dum teneo assiduas me mea cura vias:
Non pedibus terram contingo: sed ante Tonantem
Nectare, diuina pascor & ambrosiâ.

Addita est erudita NARRATIO M. GEORGII IOACHIMI RHETICI, de Libris Reuolutionum, atq; admirandis de numero, ordine, & distantijs Sphærarum Mundi hypothesibus, excellentissimi Mathematici, totiusq; Astronomiæ Restauratoris D. NICOLAI COPERNICI.

TVBINGÆ
Excudebat Georgius Gruppenbachius,
ANNO M. D. XCVI.

37. Title Page of Kepler's *Cosmographic Mystery*, Tübingen, 1596

toward Kepler lasted about a year and a half. Then, in the Frankfurt am Main book catalog for the spring of 1597, Ursus noticed that Kepler's *Cosmographic*
37 *Mystery*□ was in print.[6] No longer an aspiring provincial bumpkin, Kepler was now an established author in his own right. Hence, turning his cold shoulder around, and affecting a smiling face, on 29 May 1597 Ursus wrote Kepler a letter, calling him a "most distinguished man" and "his most highly esteemed friend," and also recalling that

> almost two years ago you provided me with a summary, namely, in that letter which you sent me at the suggestion and prompting of most noble Wagn.[7]

Although Kepler's summary concerned "subjects highly pleasing and thoroughly agreeable" to Ursus, he had not responded. For his silence he offered two reasons. In the first place, for some years he had been uninterruptedly investigating the question of chronology. In fact, together with his letter Ursus sent Kepler a copy of his recently published *Chronotheatrum* "in expectation of your most thoughtful judgment of it." Ursus's *Chronotheatrum* is now exceedingly rare. Although it was
38 dedicated to the reigning Emperor Rudolph II,□ it was not available commercially, and was distributed privately by Ursus himself. Its title page enumerated the six stages through which it had passed: it had been conceived by Ursus in his native Dithmarschen in 1581; thought out in Holstein in 1582; begun in Denmark in 1584; sketched out in Hesse in 1586; corrected in Alsace in 1589: and finished in Bohemia in 1597.[8] In addition to his *Chronotheatrum*, Ursus had a second reason for not answering Kepler's letter:

> With regard to the matter concerning which you informed me, investigate my thinking, and want my advice, up to the present time I have not yet reached the required decision and am still in

38. Rudolph II, Holy Roman Emperor from 1576 to 1612; by Johann von Achen (1552-1615), appointed court painter on 1 January 1592; copper engraving by Egidius Sadeler in 1603

doubt. My astronomy teacher, Jost Bürgi,[9] an expert not only in geometry but also in mechanics, half a year ago, when he was visiting his Imperial Majesty here in Prague, accidentally rather than intentionally, left me a certain little sketch (so to speak), which he had made and drawn of the Copernican hypothesis concerning the heavenly motions. Examining it afterwards, I compared it with your views about the distances between the spheres of the planets. Between his sketch and your conclusions, I for my part found not much difference (which astonished me greatly). Therefore, when I learned that your dissertations (as you wish them to be called)[10] on these topics had been published, I could not refrain from asking you for one copy, since none have been brought to us at Prague (whether by chance or through some negligence, I do not know) by our booksellers (a circumstance which I regret). Therefore please satisfy my wish in this trifle, so that I may more fully and more thoroughly learn and understand the opinion you have formed concerning this matter (the opinion which has just been made public) and whether you still want to maintain the same, or perhaps a slightly modified view.[11]

In a postscript[12] Ursus added that the year 1551 in his *Chronotheatrum* reported the hour and day of his birth, "which you ask for" (with the intention of casting an astrological horoscope). Since Kepler's letter had made no such request, it may have been transmitted to Ursus in a conversation with Wagn.

In a later letter to his actual teacher, Maestlin, who had edited the *Cosmographic Mystery* for him,[13] Kepler revealed his true opinion of Ursus:

Even though he is not in the least a serious writer, I granted his request [for the *Cosmographic Mystery*] because he is the Imperial Mathemati-

> cian, capable of helping me and harming me, since his influence extends even into Styria[14] [of which Graz was the capital].

Whereas Ursus had asked Kepler for a single copy (*exemplar unicum*) of his *Cosmographic Mystery*, in this letter to Maestlin Kepler mistakenly said that Ursus had requested copies [In the plural: *exemplaria*). Kepler thereby confused Ursus's wish with his own plan: Kepler wanted Brahe to see his *Cosmographic Mystery*. As Kepler told Maestlin in this same letter:

> I still have not been able to send Tycho a copy [of the *Cosmographic Mystery*]. I eagerly await his opinion.[15]

In sending Ursus the single copy he had requested, Kepler joined with it an additional copy, which he wanted Ursus to forward to Brahe. In exchange, if Ursus had any works by Brahe, he was asked to send them to Graz at Kepler's expense.[16] This innocent request made by an earnest young scholar intent on acquiring the writings of an acknowledged master was never answered by Ursus. He realized that Kepler had not yet heard about his fierce quarrel with Brahe (the quarrel that soon culminated in Ursus's death).

In a later letter to Maestlin, dated 8 December 1598, wherein Kepler recalled having asked Ursus to act as his forwarding agent to Brahe, Kepler mentioned other aspects of his second letter to Ursus:

> Having raised certain chronological questions, I said I was pleased that Ursus does not follow the authors of fables. I remarked that I marveled at the wide range of reading of any one who could write such a chronology. I asked him in every possible way to send me his opinion of my book, since I had undertaken to publish it in order to have discussions with experts in these matters.[17]

Kepler's recollections of what he had said in his second letter to Ursus are invaluable, because that document has not survived. It elicited no reply from Ursus, as we just saw. After several months, Kepler heard from the Styrian treasurer, who had been to Prague, that he had been praised by Ursus.[18] This report prompted Kepler's third letter to Ursus, written about December 1597 (like Kepler's second letter to Ursus, this too has not survived). In his third letter, after again requesting Ursus's opinion of the *Cosmographic Mystery*, Kepler

> chided him for his distorted abstemiousness. The money he receives from the emperor, he is in the habit of returning to the emperor (according to the gossip around here). Yet he could support those who pursue the same studies, including me. I said this by way of a joke. But there is no answer from him.[19]

In fact, Kepler received only one reply in response to his three letters to Ursus. Kepler's first letter to Ursus was ignored for a year and a half until the announcement of the publication of the *Cosmographic Mystery* reached Prague. Then Ursus promptly asked Kepler for a copy. When it arrived, it was accompanied by a copy for Brahe. That abruptly ended Ursus's participation in the correspondence with Kepler, whose second and third letters to Ursus both went unanswered.

VII

KEPLER AND HERWART

VII

KEPLER AND HERWART

Herwart, to whom Roeslin sent his private condemnation of Ursus as a plagiarist, was intensely interested in astronomy and astrology. In the ancient Roman poet Lucan's *Civil War* (I, 639-672), he encountered a passage which puzzled him. In the nebulous manner of which some poets are so fond, Lucan had placed the sun and the five then-known planets in various signs of the zodiac, without indicating the precise moment of the observation. Herwart found a pretty good match, except for Venus and Mercury. Unable to fit these two inner planets into Lucan's instantaneous chart of the heavens, Herwart appealed to various experts, including Christopher Grienberger (1561 or 1564-1636), who became the Jesuit professor of mathematics in Graz in 1597.[1] Grienberger referred Herwart's problem to Kepler.

This unexpected development offered the young Lutheran a possible avenue of escape from the impending persecution of the Protestants in Graz. If Kepler could only ingratiate himself with the local Jesuits and also with the immensely influential Catholic chancellor of Bavaria, he might be spared. Thus, when he sent Herwart his meticulously detailed analysis of the Lucan passage on 12[2] September 1597, Kepler asked for either one of two favors. In the first place, he wished to be remembered to a relative, Johann Baptist Fickler (1533-1610), a prominent figure in the Catholic Counter-Reformation.[3] Alternatively, Kepler wanted Herwart to extract from the mathematicians of his acquaintance their opinions (not necessarily favorable) of his recently published *Cosmographic Mystery*. Herwart's inquiry addressed to Graz had pleased some of the local authorities so much that Kepler thought nothing more conducive to his honor could have happened to him.[4]

He took great pains with not only the contents of his answer to Herwart, but also its presentation. He himself wrote out the preliminary draft of his discussion of Lucan on both sides of nine sheets, including his calculations. For the fair copy to be sent to Herwart, however, he hired a professional scribe. Deleting his calculations, he put the following instructions for the scribe on his draft:

> Wherever there are no deletions, in two days make a fair copy of these pages, since they have to be sent to Bavaria [the regular courier being scheduled to leave Graz two days after Kepler turned his draft over to the scribe]. I won't haggle over your wages. Write well and, above all, legibly.[5]

The draft is preserved among Kepler's papers in Leningrad. In the fair copy, which is now in the library of the University of Munich, Kepler himself wrote the covering letter to Herwart, and added a concluding paragraph to his discussion of Lucan.

This was received by Herwart in Munich on 23 October 1597. While he was happy to read Kepler's analysis, he heartily disagreed with it, as he explained in a letter written the next day.[6] In it he posed another question about ancient astronomy, suggested how the delivery of Kepler's letters to Munich could be speeded up, and promised to satisfy both of Kepler's requests. As a result, Fickler soon wrote to Kepler.[7] Had he

39. Johannes Praetorius (1537-1616), engraving by Wolfgang Philipp Kilian from his own sketch

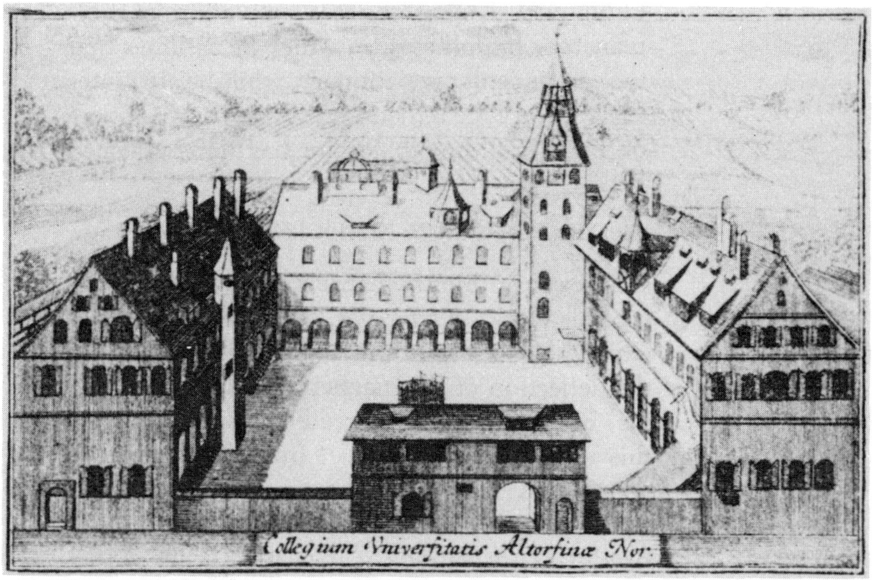

40. Altdorf, where Praetorius taught astronomy at the local university

known about Kepler's position in Graz, he would have anticipated Herwart's intermediation. Should Kepler ever write to him directly, he would like to learn the whereabouts of Kepler's paternal uncle, Sebald, a Jesuit.[8] As a further result, Johannes Praetorius□ 39
(1537-1616), professor of astronomy at the University of Altdorf,□ acknowledged receiving Kepler's *Cosmo-* 40
graphic Mystery from Herwart on 13/23 February 1598.[9] Praetorius's first impression was favorable, a fuller report would follow. In April he returned the book to Herwart, with an unsympathetic and skeptical reaction, which was intensified in May 1598.[10]

Meanwhile, on Christmas Eve, 1597, Kepler had answered Herwart. After further study of Lucan, he was convinced that the poet was describing an astrological fantasy, not an actual disposition of the heavenly bodies.[11] In his reply of 12 March 1598, Herwart referred to

> Philip van Lansberge's contemplation of new planetary hypotheses, in which he assumes that the earth's center is stationary, while he attributes to its surface the remaining motions of the sphere of the stars, although nothing has been published yet.[12]

Kepler answered on 26 March 1598:

> I have seen nothing by Lansberge [1561-1632], except his work on triangles,[13] a marvelous book, which helps me very much. From it I computed the deflection of the magnetic needle, for example, because I saw by rereading your letter that this would please you....[14] But with regard to what you write about Philip van Lansberge, Reinmarus[15] Ursus did the same thing before him: the fixed stars are stationary, the earth's center is stationary, its surface rotates around its center, and the sun (which is the center for all five planets) revolves around the earth. Magini in Italy did almost the same thing, although he also transfers to the fixed stars the motion of the surface of the earth's globe.[16]

The *Ephemerides* (Venice, 1582) of Giovanni Antonio
41 Magini□ (1555-1617) was used by Kepler to calculate
lunar eclipses.[17] But in Magini's *New Theory of the Celestial Spheres in Agreement with N. Copernicus's Observations* (Venice, 1589) Kepler could find only an absolute rejection of Copernicus's cosmology, by contrast with his observations:

> The observations of Nicholas Copernicus, a very well-informed man and most outstanding specialist, agree with the heavens marvelously, and I shall follow his observations. On the other hand, I shall ignore his hypotheses about the multiple motions of the terrestrial globe, and about the sun's immobility in the center of the universe and the immobility of the sphere of the

41. Giovanni Antonio Magini (1555-1617), professor of astronomy at the University of Bologna

stars. He devised these hypotheses most ingeniously in order to avoid a multitude of spheres. But his hypotheses are rejected by practically everybody as being absurd and too far away from the truth. For this one reason alone so great a man, to whom astronomy owes and will forever owe a gigantic debt, is mercilessly assailed by many people, even though nobody has been able thus far to produce a theory of the motions that is more suitable and more reliable than this theory of Copernicus.... I shall cling so closely to Copernicus...as to seem to have formulated in accordance with his thinking the

> nonuniformity of the angles, the sizes and arrangement of the spheres, and their distances from the earth, in a word, all the phenomena. There is, however, this one exception: in opposition to the truth and all philosophy, Copernicus regards the earth as mobile, with the sun and the eighth sphere stationary, whereas I make the opposite assumption.[18]

Whereas Copernicus regarded the eighth sphere of the stars as stationary, Magini clung to the pre-Copernican view that their daily rotation was due to the motion of the stars and not to any Copernican rotation of the earth. In this letter to Herwart, Kepler left the erroneous impression that the sun "is the center for all five planets" in the cosmology of Magini, for whom the earth remained the traditional center for the sun and the other planets. Yet in a letter to Brahe dated 13 September 1590, Magini said: "I cannot refrain from strongly approving the system of the universe devised by you."[19] Perhaps for this reason Magini was linked by Kepler with Roeslin and Brahe:

> The same idea was proposed, philosophically, however, rather than astronomically, by Roeslin in Alsace and Tycho Brahe in Denmark, who appears to be the first.[20]

In 1597 Roeslin stated, astronomically rather than philosophically, that

> The sun and the moon [revolve] around the center of the universe. But the other five planets [revolve] around another center, that is, the sun.... The sun is the center of the spheres of the five planets.

Roeslin himself characterized his

> hypotheses as agreeing with Ptolemy's hypotheses, except one, namely, the third ... 3. The sun is approximately the true center of the

> spheres of the five remaining planets [excluding the moon].[12]

Kepler summed up for Herwart:

> In short, the hypotheses are not new, but a new form, that is, a mixture of the ancient hypotheses and Copernicus's new hypotheses.... There is not an astronomer who rates these new hypotheses a hair's breadth below the ancient hypotheses. Copernicus's only quarrel, and his entire quarrel, is with natural philosophers, metaphysicians,[22] and theologians.

VIII

KEPLER AND BRAHE

VIII

KEPLER AND BRAHE

Kepler awarded the priority in propounding the new
hypotheses to Brahe. But he knew so little about him
that when he sent copies of his *Cosmographic Mystery*
to George Limnaeus,[1] professor of mathematics at the
42 University of Jena, ☐ he asked for information about
Brahe. In his reply to Kepler on 24 April/4 May 1598
Limnaeus reported:

> Brahe is descended from a family of the highest Danish nobility. Through a royal grant in the famous Danish Sound, it is said, he obtained the island Hven, which others call Scarlatina,[2] where he built a castle and observatory, Uraniburg. He has carried out observations with the greatest skill, according to the unanimous statements of all the specialists, particularly those who have spent some time with him. Among the latter, I am friendly with Nicholas Raimers Ursus of Dithmarschen and Adrian Metius, son of Adrian, of Alkmaar.[3] As far as I know, Brahe has published *Progymnasmata astronomica*, observations of the spectacular star of 1572, observations of the comet of 1577-1578...[4]

Like Kepler, Limnaeus still knew nothing about the quarrel that had broken out between Brahe and Ursus.

42. Jena, after a sketch by Dilich

Having obtained no indication from Ursus that he had forwarded the copy of the *Cosmographic Mystery* which he had received for Brahe, Kepler decided to dispense with an intermediary and communicate directly with the Danish astronomer. At about the time he wrote his third letter to Ursus, on 13 December 1597 Kepler sent his first letter to Brahe. On the assumption that Brahe, whose wealth and preeminence kept him in touch with all current developments in astronomy, already had copies of the *Cosmographic Mystery*, Kepler explained that the "difficulty of transmission over so great a distance deterred" him from sending any additional copies. But the book's potential reputation would be harmed in the absence of Brahe's criticism and praise.

> This is the reason impelling me as an obscure person to write you a letter from this little-known corner of Germany. In keeping with that intense love of truth which your reputation for greatness proclaims is likewise present in you, I beseech you to explain your view of this subject with that honesty and sympathy for which you are renowned, and to inform me in a brief letter. How happy I would be if Tycho would arrive at the same conclusion as Maestlin! With these two supporters I shall not hesitate courageously to withstand the opposition that has already been aroused on all sides. If, however, the outcome is that you decide to censure the feeble, inept, and childish remarks such as have escaped me in large numbers on account of my immaturity, would I not on the other hand prefer such blame to the approval, it might be, of the whole world?.... None of your works reaches us. What I knew about you, I had learned from Maestlin. You will therefore forgive me if I do you and your hypothesis any harm in the passages where I mention your name.[5] My respect restrains me from saying and asking anything further. To an individual

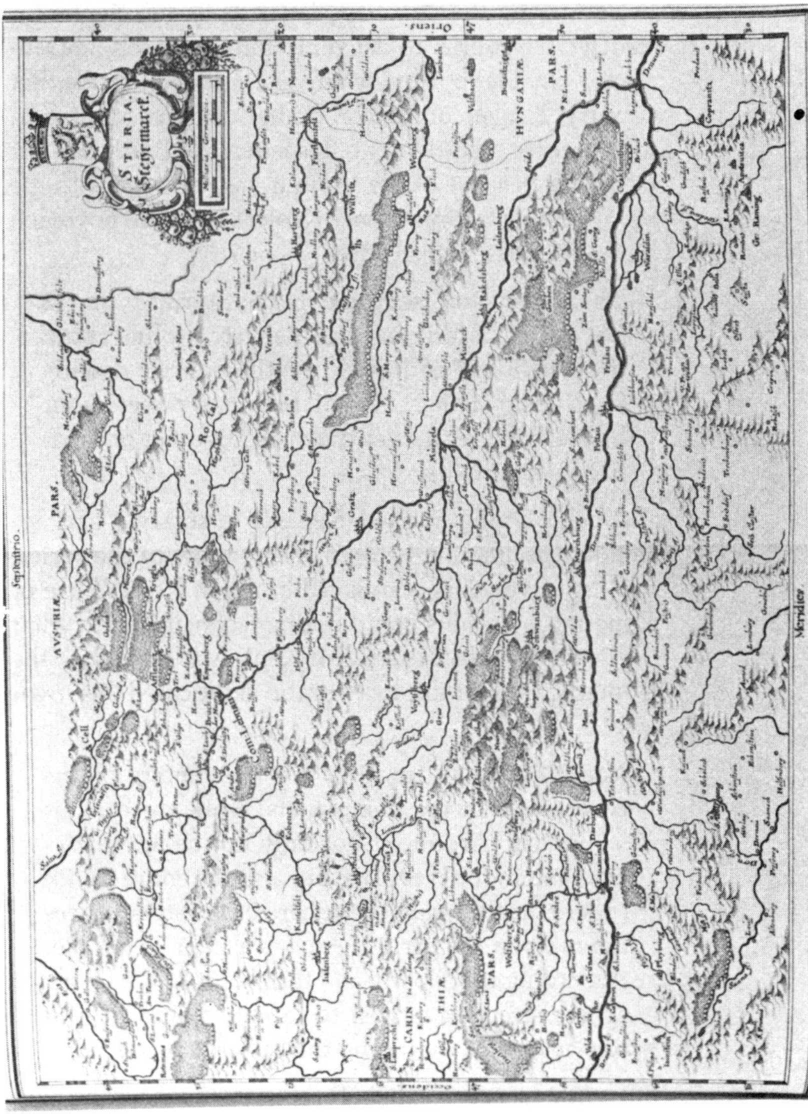

43. Styria, an Austrian province; on stylistic grounds this engraving may be attributed to Matthaeus Merian Sr.

> struggling along, open up the road by writing to me very briefly. For you will make me show you how much more I want to learn than to be praised.[6]

In addressing this, his first, letter to Brahe, Kepler instructed the courier to deliver it "into his hands, in Denmark." Unable to provide any exact address inside that country, Kepler counted on Brahe's national reputation to guarantee the delivery of his letter. But Brahe had left Denmark because of the strain in his relations with the royal administration. Hence Kepler's letter did not reach him until early March 1598.

> 43 The letter you sent me from Styria□ on 13 December of last year was delivered to me about the beginning of March by the courier coming from Helmstedt.... I had previously seen your book... and read it, as much as my other occupations permitted.[7]

Although Brahe praised Kepler's terse style and ingenious speculation, his own observations over a period of thirty-five years convinced him that Kepler's use of Copernicus's results could not be reconciled with what the heavens revealed. Against Kepler's adherence to the Copernican cosmology,[8] Brahe advocated his own
44 view: □

> Near the sun in motion are the centers of the revolutions of the five planets, while the earth is stationary. Around it not only do the luminaries [sun and moon] revolve, but also the entire eighth sphere (as they call [the sphere of the stars]) gazes down upon the earth, which is also in its middle. According to Copernicus, the extent of the starry sphere stretches almost to infinity,[9] even by this one absurdity shattering this sphere's position.

But with regard to their future relations, Brahe was quite friendly toward Kepler:

NOVA MVNDANI SYSTEMATIS HYPOTYPOSIS AB AUTHORE NUPER ADINUENTA, QUA TUM VETUS ILLA PTOLEMAICA REDUNDANTIA & INCONCINNITAS, TUM ETIAM RECENS COPERNIANA IN MOTU TERRÆ PHYSICA ABSURDITAS, EXCLUDUNTUR, OMNIAQUE APPARENTIIS CŒLESTIBUS APTISSIME CORRESPONDENT. 189

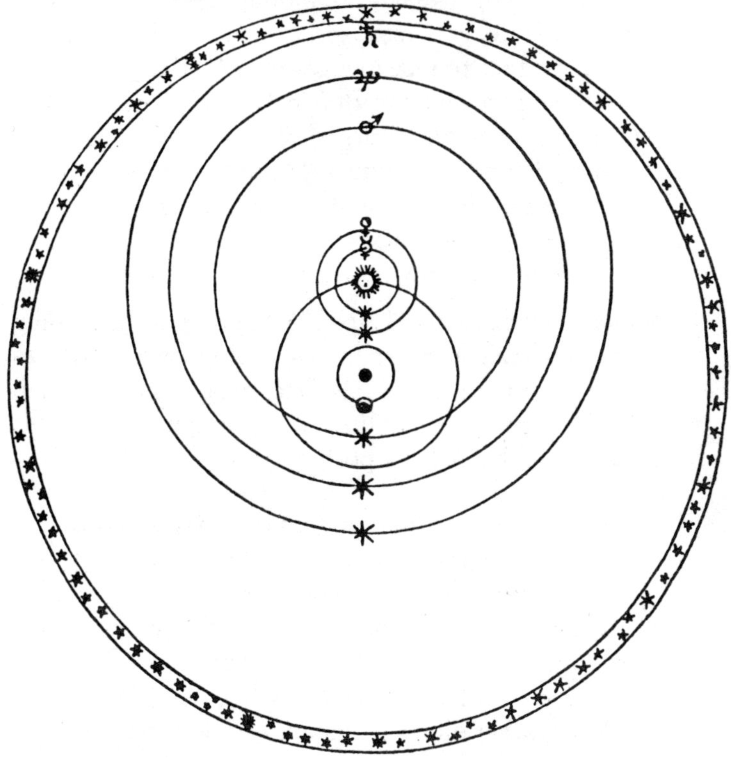

44. Brahe's Cosmos

> To the extent that I can help your arduous undertakings in this matter, you will find me not at all hard to please, especially if you visit me at some time now that I am living in Germany. I have come here from my native country with my whole family to avoid the destruction of so great an astronomical treasure accumulated by the expenditure of sweat and money over so many years. Here you may discuss such lofty topics with me face to face in an agreeable and pleasant manner. Farewell. Written in Wandsbek only half a mile from Hamburg,[10] in Rantzau's castle, where I am now living. My astronomical apparatus and my entire library equipment having been brought here from Denmark, I am no less attentive to heavenly matters than previously.[11]

Brahe dated this letter "1 April 1598, old style," according to the Julian calendar then used in Protestant countries, as the equivalent of 11 April 1598, according to the Gregorian calendar introduced by the papacy in 1582. Below his signature Brahe added a postcript:

> I do not know by what chance it happened that the same courier who brought me your [letter]
> 45 from Helmstedt □ at the same time also delivered to me from the same place a defamatory and criminal publication, tied together with your letter, and written by a certain wild Ursus ["bear," in Latin] rather than a real man. I could run through the insolent chicaneries and shocking lies and insults with which his publication abounds to excess and beyond all shame. Yet I also found there a certain brief letter by you,[12] with which he strives to adorn himself and conceal his misdeeds. When I had read your letter, I was astonished that you make so much of him. But I excused your error because you would not commit it except on the basis of hearsay and that publication which he

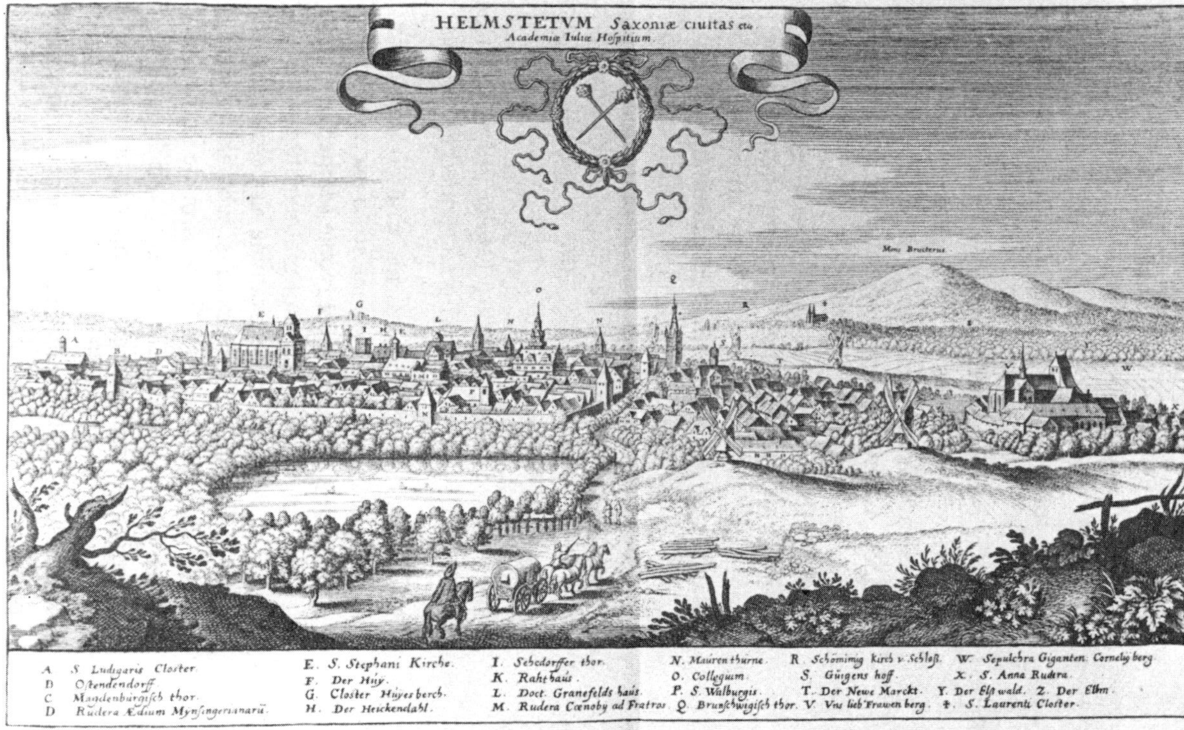

45. Helmstedt, site of the university named after its founder; engraving by Matthaeus Merian Sr. in or before 1641

calls the *Foundation of Astronomy*. He has practically nothing in it which is his own. Everything is rather snatched and stolen from others, as is his habit. He is convicted of the plagiarism with which I charge him in my hypotheses not only by the crude blunder which he committed in drawing the sphere of Mars[13] but also by many others which I shall expose at the proper time. I also still have a certain notebook of what he secretly copied when he was in the service of a certain Danish nobleman [Eric Lange], a relative of mine, in 1584, when Ursus was with him in Uraniburg. There he acted no differently. For my part, I had devised this system of hypotheses long before. I would not have inserted it in my book on the comet of 1577, had I not been afraid of such plagiarists, who had learned about the system from those around me. I am also amazed that you call it his hypothesis, although not only in your book but in this letter too [of 13 December 1597 to Brahe] you ascribe it to me (not undeservedly).[14]

In his *Cosmographic Mystery* Kepler did not ascribe any hypothesis to Brahe, who continued as follows:

Meanwhile you also sing his praises mightily. Would that you had not done so to excess! In the address you call him "Most Noble Mathematician" (I shall not say what kind of mathematician he is; as for his nobility, if you examine his descent, he is from the Dithmarschen peasants, who also despise him). Then you say that "he was made known to you by his most illustrious glory, in which he alone outstrips the astronomers of this age as much as Phoebus's orb [outshines] the tiny stars." You would have added more [compliments] had time permitted. Yet how skillfully you excuse even further [flattery] because "longwindedness is not becoming to astronomers." I do not know whether you then silently experienced within yourself any such feeling, whereas this attitude was prompted by a scheme. In addition, [you remark] that "all scholars think a great deal of him." You call him your "teacher," you attribute my "hypotheses" to him. And at the end you conclude that he may flourish as the "pride of Germany for the sake of the stars" (of which he has a very limited knowledge) "and of science" (which, if he knows any, he scrapes together and filches for himself here and there).

You apparently wrote such things about a nobody heedlessly. For my part, I have no objection at all. Indeed, I would prefer them to be true, or somebody honored who deserved such lofty praise in astronomy and mathematics. I would not be the last to celebrate his glory. Yet I would not elevate him above Ptolemy or Copernicus, and other distinguished men such as Maestlin is in Germany now, unless I considered that he would be deserving after an adequate examination. Yet however this may be, it surely does not condone his misuse of your letter in that book in which he vilifies me. His misuse is such that he wants your letter to purge him, as it were, and prove how great he is and how highly he is to be regarded (if it please the gods), while praising himself so excessively, flattering himself, and implicitly downgrading others.

But you wrote these things through ignorance when you were young. Maybe you had not thought that he would ever publish that letter, much less ever misuse it to mock and insult others. That is why I am rather calm in this affair.

Nevertheless, I would like you to deposit with me at the earliest possible moment a statement indicating whether you are satisfied with his behavior and what you think of his poisonous publication; and later on, the opinion of other scholars into whose hands it has arrived. For I

> have no doubt that it has reached your area, having been printed in Prague with the name of the printer suppressed, as happens in libelous books. I add nothing further about this matter, since it does not merit being discussed at length. It is up to you to make a sincere evaluation of this postscript and consign this sheet to the flames.[15]

The title page of Ursus's *De astronomicis hypothesibus* (Prague, 1597) stated that the book was obtainable from the author (*apud autorem*) and had no official authorization (*absque omni privilegio*). Yet Ursus had applied for, and on 22 August 1596 had received, an author's privilege for astronomical writings.[16] When Ursus decided in the summer of 1596 to respond to Brahe's *Astronomical Letters,* he planned to stay within the bounds of propriety, as is indicated by his application for a privilege. But that document served no useful purpose, since no censor would ever have approved what Ursus actually wrote in his *Astronomical Hypotheses.*

IX

BRAHE AND MAESTLIN

AD CLARISSIMVM VIRVM
D. IOANNEM SCHONE-
RVM, DE LIBRIS REVOLVTIO
nū eruditissimi viri, & Mathema
tici excellentissimi, Reuerendi
D. Doctoris Nicolai Co-
pernici Torunnæi, Ca-
nonici Varmien-
sis, per quendam
G Rheticus. Iuuenem, Ma-
thematicæ
studio
sum
NARRATIO
PRIMA.

ALCINOVS.

Δεῖ δ' ἐλευθέριον εἶναι τῇ γνώμῃ τὸν μέλλοντα φιλοσοφεῖν

46. George Joachim Rheticus (1514-1574), *First Report*, Gdańsk, 1540, title page describing the author only as a young student of mathematics; presentation copy to Johann Schöner (1477-1547), who identified the author as G. Rheticus

IX

BRAHE AND MAESTLIN

In rebuking Kepler for overpraising Ursus, Brahe referred to "other distinguished men such as Maestlin is in Germany now." Some three weeks later, on 21 April/ 1 May[1] 1598, Brahe wrote to Maestlin:

> I recently received from Styria a certain learned publication by the excellent mathematician Johannes Kepler. In it he tries by quite a brilliant speculation to fit the revolutions of the planets in the Copernican arrangement symmetrically with the five regular solids. With regard to this subject he also wrote to me recently, and I in turn explained to him my own opinion of these matters, to the extent permitted by the pressure of my obligations.
>
> I see, however, that in the same book you somewhat hesitantly make some references to the hypothesis which I devised many years ago.[2]

As the editor of Kepler's *Cosmographic Mystery*, Maestlin included in the volume a reprint of Rheticus's *First Report*, □ and in an Address to the Reader of 46
Rheticus, Maestlin remarked:

> Quite recently some very outstanding astronomers . . . in agreement with the ancient hypotheses place the stationary earth in the

> center of the sphere of the moon and the stars as well as the entire universe, but in agreement with Copernicus they [make] the sun the center of the other planets' [spheres], yet they assert that it is movable.[3]

This is the kernel of Brahe's hypothesis, for which he sought priority. Hence he chided Maestlin:

> You attribute it promiscuously also to others by paying too much heed perhaps to my plagiarists. With regard to the same subject, you also make several inferences. Had you considered them more carefully, and examined from all sides my view and all the reasons for the formation of this hypothesis, you would perhaps have refrained from such hesitations. Yet if you retain any doubt about this discovery, I am ready to remove it and explain the whole subject quite thoroughly. The facts themselves will also be decisive, when you learn that I have set forth the motions of the planets so precisely in this scheme that there is nothing further demanded by the senses. Yet in the same little book you apparently not only doubt about the advancement of astronomy but also abandon the effort, although previously you had other hopes.[4]

Yet in his Address to the Reader, Maestlin praised the positive features of Kepler's *Cosmographic Mystery:*

> These can never be obtained or expected in the ancient hypotheses or in the modifications made by the more recent astronomers. Who, therefore, will we believe is to be trusted with greater confidence? Those who in a desire to avoid some manifest absurdities rush into more serious [difficulties] which, however, they prop up on shaky foundations, while saying nothing reasonable, or he who asserts nothing without good reason, establishes everything solidly, and thoroughly refutes what seems absurd?[5]

Brahe doggedly opposed Maestlin's complete rejection of his cosmology and unqualified support of Kepler's:

> Suppose that astronomy is going to be reconstructed in advance, as you suggest, by measurements based on those regular solids rather than on precise observations made afterwards. We shall surely wait in vain too long, if not indeed forever, before anybody can furnish any such result. The determination of the size of these regular solids, if it were to be accepted throughout, ought to be based on and proved by earlier observations. In like manner, with the exception of the more general features, all the details cannot be obtained from this source with the required accuracy.[6]

Brahe then proceeded to list several shortcomings in the numerical details of the competing astronomical systems, including Kepler's. He concluded by saying:

> When I found out that the courier was going to spend this whole day in Hamburg, I arranged to have a copy made of Kepler's letter to me together with my reply, to be added to this letter.[7]

These three documents arrived by way of Strasbourg on 29 May/7 June 1598, as Maestlin noted in his characteristically methodical manner.[8] In the course of his regular correspondence with Kepler, on 4/14 July 1598 he informed his former pupil at the end of a long letter:

> Lastly, I received a letter from the most noble Tycho Brahe, in which he defends his point of view tenaciously. He wrote to me very cordially. I would have sent you a copy, but there was no time to duplicate [his letter]. However, I shall send [you a copy] at the very earliest opportunity. His letter contains not-a few noteworthy things. But even though they have no little effect on me, nevertheless your interdigitation of the

> heavenly bodies with the five regular solids affects me much more. Brahe also added a copy of your letter written to him and of his answer to you, in which again there are not a few noteworthy items. Moreover, I cannot overlook what he writes about Ursus.
>
> I understand that Ursus published a certain book [*On Astronomical Hypotheses*] in which he rails at Tycho with the foulest jibes. In the front matter he placed a letter written by you, in which you whitewash him with the most lavish praise. I have not seen the book, however, nor can I believe that you wrote such a letter.[9]

From Brahe, Maestlin had received a copy of his letter to Kepler of 1 April 1598. Therein Brahe declared that Ursus "strives to adorn himself" with Kepler's letter of 15 November 1595. Since such letters were often placed in the front matter of a book, Maestlin assumed that Ursus had placed Kepler's letter in the front matter (*praefixit*) of his *Astronomical Hypotheses*.[10] Actually, it is at sig. Dlr-v. But of course Maestlin had not yet seen Ursus's book. In his letter to Kepler of 4/14 July 1598, Maestlin proceeded to remind his former pupil of what he had told him about Ursus:

> For you know my opinion of that man. What he published in his little book [*Foundation of Astronomy*] is not his own thinking. He does not even understand it, so that what is right in his book, he propounds with the wrong words. He takes a lot from Tycho and advertises it as his own. I showed you this in Tycho's book [*Stella caudata*]. Ursus's trigonometry contains nothing remarkable which is not written better elsewhere. What is noteworthy in it, however, he himself does not understand, hence he propounds it incorrectly and awkwardly, etc. It would therefore seem surprising to me if you elevated him above the stars in this way. He would accordingly

deserve your exoneration of yourself in opposition to him on the ground that he so grossly abuses your kindness, since I frankly do not believe that you honored him with decorations of this kind.[11]

X

URSUS AS IMPERIAL MATHEMATICIAN

47. Uelzen, birthplace of Caspar Lehmann (1563/5-1622); engraving by Matthaeus Merian's heirs, after a sketch by Konrad Bruno (†1671)

X

URSUS AS IMPERIAL MATHEMATICIAN

The contempt felt by Brahe, Kepler, and Maestlin for Ursus's discussions of astronomy and mathematics was not known in Prague, then the capital of the Holy Roman Empire. The reigning emperor, Rudolph II, a patron of the arts and sciences, was fervently devoted to astrology. Taking advantage of this obsession, common among rulers of the time, Ursus gained appointment as Imperial Mathematician, whose principal occupation was casting the horoscopes of political leaders. One of his colleagues was Rudolph II's gem cutter, Caspar Lehmann□ of Uelzen (1563/5-1622), 47
who married Regina, the sister of George Rollenhagen.[1] In April 1598 George Rollenhagen sent a letter to Brahe, who had a copy made of it. The copyist omitted the date and place of writing, which are not known since the original has not been preserved. But the copyist did note that the letter had been received at the beginning of May 1598. Accompanying the letter was a copy of the *Astronomical Hypotheses* by Ursus, concerning whom Rollenhagen passed along to Brahe what he had learned from Lehmann:

> For some years I have had at the court of His Imperial Majesty among the principal functionaries a relative from Lüneburg, Caspar Lehmann, a

gem cutter by profession, but at the same time a student of everything, especially astrology. Since he likes me for this reason, he also visits me from time to time, as he did not so many weeks ago. In the course of the private conversation, mention was made in passing of Ursus of Dithmarschen. He said that Ursus now has the title of Imperial Mathematician, even though in his costume and character he is a bear. He has privately given to some people a little book in which he excoriates you in an unworthy manner. I therefore asked the man to send me that book, and he did. I entrusted it to a certain friend of mine, and marked the main chapters for him to copy out for me, because I was very busy. Through his negligence it fell into the hands of others and was completely lost to us. On the day before Easter [21 March 1598], when your letter was delivered to me from Hamburg about your plan to enter into an arrangement with the emperor, my courier returned from Prague, bringing another copy of the same insults with him, as I had asked my relative in writing. Had you seen it, I think it impossible that you would not have made some mention of it in a letter to me. So receive the first copy through me.... At my present age I have read many disagreements of ancient and modern philosophers, even about things hotly disputed by them, but never a book more insolent and more impertinent. Doubtless it will annoy you no little, as struggles over priority are most bitter. But what will you do? This I surely know, that if I wrestle with dung, win or lose, I am always defiled.[2]

Some two months later, on 18 June 1598, Rollenhagen transmitted to Brahe additional information which he had received from Lehmann, who had written from Prague on 21/31 May 1598:

48. Michael the Brave (c. 1558-1601), Rumania's national hero, voivode of Wallachia, aged 43

> After my brother-in-law [Rollenhagen] wrote to
> me about Ursus, I made a little inquiry here
> among His Majesty's servants, whether Ursus
> may be in disfavor with His Majesty. I received
> the report that he is not exactly in disfavor, but
> that he previously was high and mighty, and now
> is not to be seen, and in astrology does not
> understand the smallest matter. Hence it hap-
> pened that he was examined by His Majesty with
> regard to the horoscope of the Prince of
> 48 Siebenbürgen, □[3] in which he knew neither the
> beginning nor the end. Accordingly he was
> despised and mocked. Since he did not establish
> the outcome and the truth, and his judgment was
> false, now he wants to write against astrology,
> and rails against it and ridicules it in the highest
> degree, it is all lies and deception, although at first
> he praised it and thereby was brought to His
> Majesty. The second reason is that he was asked
> why he so represented himself at the court and
> 49 cast the horoscope of His Majesty's brother, □ of
> blessed memory,[4] (which turned out right) and
> now is against astrology, and he did not know
> what to answer. But it was discovered that he did
> not make it himself but took it from the books of
> Elias of Prussia and pretended that it was his. I
> have also learned that Tycho Brahe is coming
> here to our court, and His Majesty has a strong
> desire for him and will give him a castle three
> miles from Prague to establish his residence there,
> a very fine place called Brandeis.[5]

Ursus's success in forecasting Archduke Ernest's fate was followed by his failure regarding the volatile voivode, Michael the Brave. The Imperial Mathematician's consequent condemnation of astrology as all lies and deception ran counter to the emperor's unshakable conviction that astrology, if conducted correctly, controlled the key to the future. The accusation that Ursus plagiarized his prediction of what would happen to the

Ertz Herzog Ernst von Österreich 30
Gubernator der Nider Burgundiſchen Länder

49. Archduke Ernest of Austria (1553-1595), Rudolph II's younger brother

emperor's brother undermined the Imperial Mathematician's defense against Brahe's contention that Ursus had stolen his cosmological system. Brahe's impending arrival in response to the emperor's invitation cast a long shadow over Ursus's tenure as Imperial Mathematician.

The imperial invitation was hastened when Brahe's elder son delivered a sumptuous copy of his father's
50 *Astronomiae instauratae mechanica*, □ dedicated to Rudolph II on the day before New Year's, 1598.[6] In the course of that year Tycho Brahe presented a copy to Rollenhagen. The presentation was printed in the *Hamburgische Berichte von gelehrten Sachen*, 1750, p. 572, whence it was repeated at pages 146-149 in Georg Gottfried Küster's reprint, under the title *Bilder-Sammlung* (Berlin, 1751),[7] of Martin Friedrich Seidel's *Icones* (1671). The presentation copy itself was formerly owned by the Berlin Gymnasium zum grauen Kloster, but was destroyed in World War II.[8]

50. Title Page of Brahe's *Astronomiae instauratae mechanica*, Wandsbek, 1598

XI

KEPLER AND MAESTLIN

XI

KEPLER AND MAESTLIN

When Maestlin wrote to Kepler on 4/14 July 1598, he sent the letter to Graz by way of Ulm. But it became entangled with letters headed for a different destination. When the mistake was discovered there, Maestlin's letter had to be redirected, and it took many months to reach Kepler, who could not answer until 29 November / 8 December 1598:

> To the letter which you wrote on 4 July, although I should have replied in the month of August, I am replying in the month of December.... What you wrote on 4 July, you directed to Ulm. Our [courier] Jacob did not know that, because it was tied together with other letters destined for Carinthia. When he came to Carinthia and was about to make that climb again, he noticed his error when that package was opened by the individual to whom it was addressed. Jacob therefore forwarded your letter to Styria, while he himself went on to Swabia.... The courier who had been mentioned to you by Jacob was scared away (as I am absolutely convinced) from proceeding to Styria by the subsequent turn of events.[1]

This deliberately vague reference to the persecution of the Protestants in Styria precedes an extensive discussion of several chronological and astronomical topics, after which Kepler reviews his relations with Ursus. He begins this review by inadvertently misdating his first letter to Ursus: "I wrote to Ursus in the year 1595, in the summer (*aestate*), before I went to Tübingen." He should have said "winter," since he wrote on 15 November 1595 and left Graz early in February 1596, with the intention of conferring with Maestlin in Tübingen.[2] In his letter to Maestlin of 29 November/ 8 December 1598, Kepler continued to recount his relations with Ursus:

> I was urged [to write] by one of the nobles, Wagn. Since he makes frequent trips to Prague, he came to know the man and has a very high regard for him. The theme was virtually the same as in my letter to Tycho [of 13 December 1597]: since he is a widely known man, from whose writings I may learn (as much as I could know by skimming through them lightly), therefore as a pupil and a youth I sought from him, as an older man, his judgment about the matter of the five solids, which I sketched with very few words and numbers. If there is any adulation here, the blame for it is borne by the splendor of the imperial court and by his follower Wagn, who urged me on. A year and a half later [on 29 May 1597] he replied, asking for copies [actually, one copy, *exemplar unicum*] of my book, and he sent his *Chronotheatrum*, in an affable manner. I answered, I sent copies. If I added any praise (I am not sure, since I had just finished writing to you), this was done, I believe, on account of that previous letter[3] [of early October 1597 to Maestlin].

Kepler then told Maestlin (as we saw in Chapter VI at note 17) about his renewed request of Ursus's judgment of his *Cosmographic Mystery,* and for Ursus's intermediation with Brahe. In the absence of any reply from Ursus, Kepler wrote to him a third time, again without eliciting any response.

> If I praised him to his face, he is mistaken in transferring to his character and spirit what I attributed to his mind. It was no concern of mine to accuse him of what he had stolen from the works of others. I pleaded my own case. But anybody who had declared himself to be Ursus's pupil is well off to be displayed publicly as a judge between Ursus and Tycho. I congratulate myself on the honor granted to me, which I shall frankly use hereafter. He heard from a pupil. Why is he happy? Had he called me a judge, perhaps he would have heard something different. Over a letter which I dash off,[4] a big fuss is made by those whose pupil I acknowledge myself to be for the sake of honoring them.
>
> Very well, my letters are going to be valuable, I shall write carefully, I shall keep copies [as Kepler had not done in the case of his three letters to Ursus]... He harms good men; he abuses the generosity of those who write courteously rather than sincerely, for the purpose of implementing his own madness. His misdeed is aggravated by his zeal to dishonor by means of my words a very great man whom he sees that I admire. I let lawyers discuss his crime. But why do I need to write to him? For he is a seriously deranged man, as I see, who deserves to be avoided lest he continue to do harm. He evidently did this to injure me no less than Tycho. For although at first he praised me, afterward having learned that I respect Tycho, he became angry and made me the butt of these

> jeers and jests. Would that I might see that monster, who carries that letter of mine around on his horns! I shall absolutely avoid the man, however, and when the opportunity presents itself, I shall clear myself with regard to Tycho, and I also ask you to do the same. Have a copy sent to me of my letter as printed. For even though now I no longer remember the words after such a long interval, nevertheless I shall readily recognize whether he violated what I wrote and, furthermore, whether perhaps he attributes to me words which are not mine. I cannot believe that I expended so much sweat in praising him that the jackass can justly strut around.[5]

Kepler's letter to Maestlin of 29 November/ 8 December 1598 was received by the addressee in Tübingen on 10/20 January 1599, in the evening after a busy day at the university.[6] At that time Maestlin could not read the whole letter (which is nearly 600 lines long as printed in the best modern edition). But on the very next day, 11/21 January 1599, Maestlin started to write a lengthy letter to Kepler, in which he said:

> I am indeed surprised that the letter of the most noble Tycho [sent to Kepler from Wandsbek on 1/11 April 1598] has not yet reached you. I am therefore sending you a copy of it, and also a part of the letter which was sent to me.[7]

Maestlin refers to the letter which was sent to him by Brahe on 21 April 1598. But after writing throughout the whole night until nearly dawn of 12 January 1599, Maestlin misdated Brahe's letter 25 April.[8]

> The earlier part of this letter need not be copied in my opinion, because it contains

> nothing special, except that Brahe urges me to continue to write, as I had promised several years ago, and so forth. He offers his good will. But he absolutely cleaves to his hypothesis, which he upholds tenaciously. He says, however, that he explained the arguments in the letter he sent to you. He therefore had complete confidence that I would some day receive a copy of it from you (for at first he did not want to send me a copy of it, undoubtedly because he seemed to be precluded by [lack of] time). At the end he added: since the courier was unexpectedly going to spend that day in Hamburg, Brahe therefore wanted to transmit to me also a copy of the letter sent to you, and so forth. Hence, if this had been done, I note that it must have gone completely astray.[9]

After summarizing some of Brahe's views and his scriptural opposition to Copernicanism, Maestlin continued:

> I too have not seen the book by the wild Bear rather than a real man (as Tycho calls him). From this letter of Tycho, however, you may see whether you recognize your own words. But if he spuriously added more words to yours (as I am of course absolutely convinced), you will be able not only to absolve yourself with regard to Tycho (for this very reason I too have delayed answering Tycho until I should learn something definite about this matter from you) but also to seek an opportunity either by a letter or in another way of reproaching Ursus with this. I believe, however, that you do not lack advice or an advisor there [in Graz]. Manifestly he is a seriously deranged man, that true and wild Bear.[10]

XII

KEPLER, BRAHE, AND MAESTLIN

XII

KEPLER, BRAHE, AND MAESTLIN

It did not take Kepler long to act on Maestlin's suggestion that he should write again to Brahe:

> From a letter of Maestlin, which he sent me last August [when Kepler received Maestlin's letter of 4/14 July 1598,] I learned that you replied to my letter [to Brahe of 13 December 1597] and that Maestlin has a copy of that reply [of 1/11 April 1598]. At the next opportunity [8 December 1598, on account of the miscarriage of Maestlin's letter of 4/14 July 1598] I urged him to send me that copy, since your letter was not delivered to me. Thus, by chance and as a result of your diligence it happened that, even though your letter went astray, nevertheless I found out after ten months what you wanted me to know.[1]
>
> I have informed you about this at the outset lest, from this delay of ten months, you should develop a greater suspicion of guilt with regard to me. By God, in that most just quarrel of yours you demand that I should explain my point of view to you at the very earliest time. Hence, as regards my letter to Ursus, most of the words which you quoted I acknowledge are mine. Consequently, even

> though I practically shudder at some about which I am doubtful, nevertheless I cannot deny any of them. In this area, therefore, there is still no criminal act by Ursus that is manifest. But whether he published my entire letter is very doubtful to me. This would readily be resolved if I had a printed copy. For in the same letter I expressed my desire to read your works, and I asked Ursus to act in this matter.[2]

Having kept no copies of his letters to Ursus, Kepler here confuses his first letter to Ursus of 15 November 1595, which made no reference to Brahe, with his second letter, in which he asked Ursus to send him Brahe's works.[3]

> God almighty, how great and how manifold are the injuries inflicted on me by the wild man! I was soliciting his friendship by sending the letter. If he accepted my request, I miss his good faith; but if he rejected it, he is still churlish. The conversations of friends, even more their letters, ought to be confidential. He published it; he did not consult me; nor did he inform me that he would publish it, nor that he had published it; nor did he send me a copy. Those who are fair in their dealings do not venture to do any such thing even to an enemy. He might have sent me what the ancients called a dismissal, or he might have destroyed the sheet if he did not like his friend. Yet if the letter which he finally wrote to me in the second year thereafter [on 29 May 1597], if his opinion of me, can be trusted, the situation pleased him, and he had begun to cultivate my friendship. But these are trivial matters; the publication is a more grievous outrage, which should certainly be punished legally, if there is either hope or

> pleasure in a tribunal. For, what I wished to be addressed to someone doing mathematics, he connects with his vilifying, as you describe it.[4] What is most painful of all is that the man who, as he learned from my letter, is very highly regarded by me was dishonored as much as Ursus could by means of that very letter of mine. Thus he undoubtedly took pleasure in avenging himself on me for praising his enemy.[5]

Again Kepler confuses, or rather conflates, his first and second letters to Ursus.

> Yet I cannot marvel enough at the man's strategy, while I expose my own plan for that exaggerated eulogy. Why does he make such a big fuss over those laudations of mine? But of what man? If he were manly, he would disregard them. If he were wise, he would not peddle them. As somebody unknown, I was looking for a famous trumpeter of my newborn discovery. I was begging alms from him; behold, he snatched alms from the beggar. I called him "teacher"; verily, he makes a tiny addition to the eulogy from the praise of a pupil. Let him seek the laudations of those who declare themselves his teachers. But if he assigns the part of the judge to me (he could not have done so more openly than by publicizing my little letter in this way) he should know that a disposition other than a pupil's suits me now. Praise of any kind is tolerated in a pupil, if in his teacher's opinion it springs from affection and is directed toward the purpose of learning. In a judge, adulation is a crime. These things should be written, I thought, so that even though for the sake of security it is better that each most harmful remark arouses the least wrath against me, yet

if your reputation could not be safeguarded otherwise, you would have the authority to proceed publicly against a published libel. Let us, however, finally dismiss him. For the question is not how badly he behaved, but how well I behaved. And there are indeed in that letter of mine very many things which should be defended, some excused, and others freed from the worst suspicion.

Let us begin with what is most serious, namely, that you charge me with praising him to his face in contradiction to my feelings.[6] In so doing, you speak in such a way that you seem to attribute to me the most definitive judgment of others. If I remove this suspicion from myself, as it is exceedingly easy to do, I shall in my opinion have carried out a large part of my exculpation. For to discuss what sort of man Ursus is provides no pleasure now, and certainly not when I wrote that letter, and was rather immature in my judgment and had for a long time attributed quite a bit to him. A certain scholar[7] on his way back from Italy came to Graz. He showed me Ursus's book [*Foundation of Astronomy*], which he let me have for three days, and I leafed through it hastily. I find in it diagrams dedicated to the foremost mathematicians of this period. In the dedication I find a splendid call to undertake something similar, the building of astronomy from the foundations. I find certain valuable summaries, which I remembered were proclaimed by Maestlin in Tübingen. I find the theory of sines, trigonometry, well known, I suppose, but mostly[8] new to me, so that you[9] may see with what oarsman he beats his way to fame. For afterwards I found very many things in Euclid and Regiomontanus,[10]□ which I attributed to him at 51

51. Johannes Regiomontanus (1436-1476), greatest astronomer of the fifteenth century

> that time. Nor should you fear that what I just said cannot be consistent with my discovery. Let Maestlin himself say in support of me on what a shaky foundation I started in the beginning. Indeed had he sent me out in the second grade as undeveloped as I was when he sent me out in the first grade in the year [15]94,[11] he would never have given me such an excellent recommendation (to which, however, I shall be inferior as long as I live).[12]

Kepler was studying at the University of Tübingen to become a clergyman. But in his last year (the "first," as it was called) Graz needed a teacher of mathematics, and Maestlin gave him a glowing recommendation.

> Hence, with that type of education, I was encouraged to form an exalted opinion of Ursus. Afterwards I met certain Styrian noblemen, who were amateur astronomers. Because they often had to spend some time at the emperor's court, they knew Ursus. They extolled the man's intellect, his discoveries. They urged me to try to get to know him. They promised to help. On the other hand, some described him to me as a sort of Diogenes, from whom nothing could be extracted except at his pleasure or with some impropriety.[13] Shortly afterward I made my discovery.[14] There was no astronomer nearer to me to whom I should write more conveniently. When I was moved to write, for the foregoing reasons I shaped the style partly to the man's nature, as it was reported, partly to those energetically compact letters which I was reading entirely by chance at that time.[15] Out of fresh love of my discovery, my spirits soared to exultation with confidence in this outcome. Thus if anything slipped out of me slightly grander

> than my feelings about him by way of thanks to his trumpeters and by reason of my own self-esteem, all this is youthful thoughtlessness, and I offer no other excuse, provided that I wipe away the suspicion of wrongdoing. From what I have said you see, in the first place, that in good conscience I attributed to him the glory in which he seemed to rule in the court of the emperor and among the mathematicians whom he addressed in his little book [*Foundation of Astronomy*]. I find no reason, however, why I called his glory "most illustrious," except that our Illustrious [a term for the local nobility] praise him, and the Most Illustrious [Emperor] seems to praise him by keeping him at court, and because a swellhead readily descries a fly, out of which it makes an elephant.[16] With the same effect, I refer also to my saying (provided I said it) that he is thought much of by all scholars, although that would be true of some. For among the scholars I certainly included Maestlin and Tycho, who I knew did not have a very lofty opinion about him. But that I would have proclaimed even more such statements had time permitted, I do not remember promising.[17]

On 19 February 1599 Kepler forgot that on 15 November 1595 he had written *Sed nec tempus plura fert* (Time, however, does not permit more).[18]

> Indeed, that statement about longwindedness being unsuitable for astronomers was not made to excuse even more such remarks, but rather to correct the preceding remarks. But if in fact each of those words and all of them are mine, that one man alone outstrips the astronomers of this age as much as Phoebus's orb [outshines] the tiny stars, by God I inadvertently inflicted a gross

injury on many very distinguished men, and thus on my own conscience. I can declare with the utmost truthfulness that I never willingly and intentionally said in any way, seriously, jokingly, publicly, privately, insincerely or sincerely that Ursus alone is to be regarded more highly than Regiomontanus, Copernicus, Rheticus,[19] Reinhold,[20] Tycho, Maestlin, and the rest. That was never my feeling; I never wrote that with my wits about me; I never approved flattery so disgraceful. But if my authentic words have any such sound—this I do not know—the situation is to blame, I was in a hurry, and did not reread what I wrote. That whole thing, as you see, is poetic, taken from a poet, and uttered in a poetic spirit. Not only am I unwilling now, but even then when I wrote it I was unwilling that this should be distorted in another direction; I was unwilling that any interpretation should be put forward other than that Ursus stands out above the crowd, I mean, the rank and file of astronomers. This I believed, and it can be so without regard to exceptional glory. I would not protest so firmly against plain words (provided they are of this nature) unless that very letter contained absolute proof of my innocence, as indicated above. For although I am not aware in what terms I referred to Tycho, still I know that I did so [again Kepler confuses his first letter to Ursus with his second] and that the reference was such, and sprang from such an opinion as would deservedly sting Ursus, if he is so happily excited by these eulogies of himself. But as I see, I shall have to write carefully hereafter. Besides, the warning is always to pay your respects by whispering something in the bear's ear.[21]

> All the other things to which you call attention are minor. I called him "teacher," because I had dug some useful items out of his book [*Foundation of Astronomy*]. But I addressed him as "most noble," since in these provinces "learned" and a function at court are conferred on the Austrian nobility. On the other hand, I labeled the hypotheses his in which he introduced some change. For if I recall correctly, he makes the earth rotate, and with regard to Mars's circle he differs, or as you say, he errs.[22]

In his letter to Kepler of 1/11 April 1598, Brahe accused Ursus of "committing a crude blunder in drawing Mars's sphere" (where Brahe says *orbis*, Kepler says *circulo*).[23] Ursus's blunder consisted of drawing Mars's orbit completely outside the sun's annual orbit.[24] By contrast, Brahe had his sun's annual orbit intersected in two places by Mars. Kepler's letter of exculpation to Brahe continued:

> For I had previously heard from Maestlin about this difference of opinion between you and Ursus. Nevertheless, since both Magini in Italy and Roeslin in Alsace had each drawn something similar for himself from Copernicus's hypotheses, I thought that the same thing was easily devised by Ursus too. Lastly, there is nothing surprising in the agreement between the end and the beginning [of Kepler's first letter to Ursus], and there is no impropriety in the wish that "he may take care of himself, for the sake of the stars and science." As far as I am concerned, let him pursue this goal while dropping his aspersions and hollow ostentation. For me, however, the "pride of Germany" is anyone to whom I attribute as much as I attributed to him, since of course mathematics is the true pride of Germany alone. [I have written] these

> statements at such great length not only to bear witness to my grief at your just complaint, but also to make clear my judgment that what you think of me does have some effect on my self-esteem.[25]

The original of this letter from Kepler to Brahe has not been preserved. But Kepler arranged to have a copy made for transmission to Maestlin. This copy, which is now in the State Library in Stuttgart,[26] shows some corrections in Kepler's handwriting in the body of the letter, and at the close a final note, addressed to Maestlin:

> At the end I added that it did not seem worthy of Tycho's exalted status to be aroused so passionately by this slander. Let him rather permit their works to speak for each of them with confidence in what scholars will decide.[27]

Although the original of this letter must have carried a date, the copy for Maestlin did not. Neither did Kepler's preliminary draft, which is preserved in Leningrad.[28] But when Kepler later joined Brahe's staff, one of his duties was to compile an inventory of the letters written by Brahe and received by him.[29] In the inventory Kepler registered this letter to Brahe under the date 19 February 1599. On the previous day (8/18 February) Kepler had finally received the letter Brahe had sent him on 1/11 April 1598.[30] But by 8/18 February 1599 Kepler's answer to Brahe was already in the hands of a professional scribe, and therefore contained no acknowledgment of the receipt of Brahe's letter.

That receipt was acknowledged, however, in the letter which Kepler sent to Maestlin on 16/26 February 1599:

> I had barely received your letter [of 11/21 January 1599] on 3/13 February when, behold, finally on 8/18 February I also received Tycho's letter, flying to me from Wittenberg on the wings of a sparrow, I suppose.[31]

While Brahe was on his way from Wandsbek to the imperial court, he was warned that the plague was raging in Prague. He therefore took refuge in Wittenberg until he was assured that it was safe to proceed to the capital.

> What I replied to Brahe (since I see that this matter troubles you) you will learn from the attached copy. I would like you to believe, however, that I wrote the whole truth sincerely, because in itself the truth is quite safe. But the reason why I am not more outspoken against Ursus himself is partly shame, partly fear. For, having praised him so highly—to my sorrow—I cannot now suddenly revile him most abusively without being guilty of inconsistency. On the other hand, if Tycho should want to send my letter too to the printer, I would have to fear that Ursus would publish my other letters also, to disgrace me further. Where they are more moderate, he might falsify them or trick me in another way. Furthermore, I want you to know that I found out by talking to the courier (although he was not aware of his name) that Tycho is now in Wittenberg.[32]

While Brahe was in Wittenberg, on 11 January 1599 he wrote to his former assistant Longomontanus (1562-1647), as Christen Sørensen called himself after his birthplace Longberg in Jutland:

> From the letter you wrote me before you left Wandsbek, I learned that you want a position

> here in Germany in a university. Let me know whether you would like to succeed in [the University of] Prague the man who calls himself the Imperial Mathematician (for he will soon disappear, if he has not already done so).[33]

After a lengthy review of Brahe's objections to his *Cosmographic Mystery*, in his letter to Maestlin of 16/26 February 1599 Kepler remarked:

> But to bid farewell to Ursus and Tycho for the time being, I am trying to join the mission of the Estates, in order that I may go to Prague free of charge. There I shall make these accusations against Ursus to his face, not otherwise. From Prague to Wittenberg there are 30 miles,[34] which I shall traverse in order to see Tycho. May God guide my plan! For I do not know whether I may be able to gain this request.[35]

Although Kepler did not succeed in joining this mission to Prague, he did manage to see Brahe and Ursus later on.

XIII

KEPLER'S ANALYSIS OF URSUS'S "ASTRONOMICAL HYPOTHESES"

XIII

KEPLER'S ANALYSIS OF URSUS'S "ASTRONOMICAL HYPOTHESES"

In his letter to Brahe of 9/19 February 1599, Kepler indicated that he could tell whether his letter to Ursus had been published in its entirety in Ursus's *Astronomical Hypotheses*, if he had a copy of that book.[1] Almost a year earlier, on 16/26 March 1598, in a letter to Herwart, Kepler had mentioned "Reinmarus" Ursus.[2] Then on 6/16 May 1599 in a letter to Kepler, Herwart said:

> What Raymarus Ursus wrote against Tycho Brahe is hard to get hold of. Accordingly, since I suppose you do not have it, I wanted to send it to you heretofore, but it was not in my possession. It is going along with this letter, and I would like to understand your reaction to it.[3]

Kepler received Herwart's letter on 15/25 May 1599, "together with Ursus's little book."[4] His prompt reply, on 20/30 May, consisted of several sections, including a direct answer to Herwart's request:

> Because you ask for my judgment of Ursus's little book, even though I think that it is a serious matter for me to pass judgment on what others write, nevertheless I shall do so

> all the more readily in the case of this little book and of this author in particular. I have a special, and in my opinion an excellent, reason and I can imagine that this was not the least reason why you addressed this request to me. For on signature D, page 1, he published a certain letter written by me in which he is raised on high by me with the loftiest eulogies, but his adversary Tycho also is extolled very much by me.[5]

In Ursus's *Astronomical Hypotheses* the pages were not numbered consecutively. Instead, each signature or gathering was designated by a letter in alphabetic order, while the pages within each signature were numbered beginning with 1. At sig. D1, then, Ursus published Kepler's letter of 15 November 1595. This did not extol Tycho very much, it did not even mention him. Evidently, in writing to Herwart, Kepler did not reread his letter in printed form. He relied instead on his faulty memory, which conflated the printed letter not mentioning Brahe with his second letter to Ursus, which did mention Brahe but has never been printed.

> Perhaps you hoped that I would be an impartial judge in this case. But I cannot conceal from Your Excellency that I am prejudiced by a certain sympathy for one of the parties. For it is unseemly to say so, but provided we tell the truth, it is about four years since I wrote that letter to Ursus, I, who not even now have put my rattling toys aside altogether.[6]

Kepler's *nuces...reliqui* recalls *nucibus...relictis* in the *Satires* (I, 10) of the ancient Roman poet Persius. Always playful, Kepler said nothing about being over twenty-seven years old, married, and twice a father when he admitted that he had not yet left the nursery.

> Shortly before, I had read his book, which he entitled *Foundation of Astronomy*. More-

> over, Sigismund Wagn, whom I mention near the end of my letter, added praises of the man's reputation throughout Italy and Germany as well as of his extraordinary talent. Carried away by some sort of poetic fervor, I dashed that letter off in a jiffy (because the opportunity to send it off was fleeting).[7] I was propelled forward by my pen, as I recall even now, beyond the limits of reason and conscience. For if there was nothing else, this surely was too much: of my own accord I declared that "the little knowledge I have in astronomy I acquired with him, that is, his books, as my teacher."[8]

Even though Kepler is quoting from his own letter as printed, he substitutes *eruditionis* for *cognitionis*.

> I had taken some very noteworthy things from his book [*Foundation of Astronomy*]. Apart from it, I had seen no book published by him.[9]

Ursus had published two books while he was a protégé of Rantzau: *Grammatica latina Ranzoviana* (1580) and *Geodaesia Ranzoviana* (Leipzig, 1583), a book in German on surveying. Later, in Strasbourg he dedicated his *Foundation of Astronomy* to the superintendents of the Academy on 31 July 1588, and in the following year his reorganization of logic, *Metamorphosis logicae*.[10] A fifth work of Ursus not seen by Kepler was an astrological prognostication for 1593.[11] With regard to Ursus's *Foundation of Astronomy*, Kepler told Herwart,

> The main point that I intended to convey was that in this book I seemed to have found a short summary of both Euclid and Regiomontanus on triangles. I therefore copied all those rules or diagrams on one side of a half-sheet. Thereafter, setting Euclid aside, I computed the [regular] geometrical solids in accordance

with the theoretical requirements of my discovery. This is the extent to which I say that my discovery was taken from Ursus. I never could anticipate that the letter would be published. I wrote to Ursus three or four times.[12] Even so, I did not know that the letter had been published, until I found out from Maestlin that Tycho was reproaching me. That happened this past February at the very time I received the original of Tycho's [1/11 April 1598 letter to Kepler], which had been delayed somewhere for ten months. You therefore did me a very great favor by sending me Ursus's little book [*On Astronomical Hypotheses*], which I had for a long time been anxious to have. For I could not remember in every detail what I wrote, nor did it occur to me what reason most especially drove me toward such exaggerated eulogies (for there were some contributing causes). It is of grave concern to me that to a certain extent Ursus wins a victory with that letter of mine (I see no other reason why he thought it worth publishing, for as regards the scientific content of my letter, Ursus knows and admits that my little book [*Cosmographic Mystery*] is available).

Ludicrously misappropriating the approval expressed by me (a very great man, forsooth), he misuses it to embellish and support his vilifications. In this way, consciously and deliberately, without being injured by me, Ursus makes me hated by a most outstanding man (although Tycho's magnanimity in forgiving me is no less than his frankness in chiding me). By linking our discoveries inopportunely, just when my reputation is beginning, Ursus does not shrink from exposing my name to the ill-will of scholars,

> whoever they may be. As I say, you understand how grave a concern this is to me. It is therefore just as clear that I am not free from prejudice and bias. But to a certain extent Ursus himself makes me the judge in this case by bolstering his reputation with the backing of my letter. I therefore believe that I am rightfully authorized to say what I think. But why go on at length? This case will be private, with you serving as attorney for both sides in my court. I shall therefore act as the referee (although I am inept in the law).[13]

In his typically playful manner, at no matter what age, Kepler proceeded with his mock trial by distinguishing between Ursus's litigious style and his substantive claims.

> What Ursus wrote can be considered in various ways. In the first place, then, his manner of making accusations as well as his insults, whether these are retorts or are introduced of his own accord, I leave to Your Excellency to examine. For if I say that in making his charges he overstepped the bounds, the same will be imputed to me in my lavishing of praise. Although people fear cruel abuse, on the other hand they despise flattery. Hence, we may perhaps have made equal progress against both sides, so that what each objects to in the other has no legal basis.
>
> As for the quarrel which of the two swiped the other's hypotheses, I think that the absolutely correct answer will appear when and if the works of both of them are published. For, the truth will establish itself, and by its power overwhelm the opposing contention. Yet something can also be elicited from what we have. Ursus admits that his hypotheses are not his own, except to the extent that he diverges somewhat from Tycho.

Ursus's *Astronomical Hypotheses* displayed Brahe's cosmical diagram as his own, except that Ursus's stars were stationary (*coelo stante*), so that the daily rotation was performed by Ursus's earth, whereas Brahe's earth was stationary and his stars rotated diurnally.[14]

> On the other hand, Tycho maintains that all by himself he discovered the hypotheses which he propounds (where they depart from the Copernican hypotheses), and that he saw nothing similar elsewhere.[15]

In a private letter written on 21 February 1589, but published in his *Astronomical Letters* in 1596, Brahe told Rothmann:

> I did not, however, take my starting point in constructing these hypotheses by inverting[16] the Copernican hypotheses. If you ever entertained any such thought, it was not known to me, as you are well aware, nor was anything like it ever to be inferred from Rheticus or Reinhold.[17]

XIV

BRAHE, REINHOLD, AND WITTICH

52. Saalfeld, birthplace of Erasmus Reinhold, (1511-1553)

XIV

BRAHE, REINHOLD, AND WITTICH

Inverting the Copernican system was not the starting point of his own hypotheses, according to Brahe, nor was it to be inferred from Reinhold. Despite Brahe's denial, a link between himself and Reinhold has recently been proposed. In 1549 Reinhold received an imperial license[1] to publish his forthcoming commentary on the whole of Copernicus's *Revolutions* (*commentarius in totum opus*). But on 19 February 1553, at the early age of forty-two, he died of tuberculosis at his home in Saalfeld,□ with 52
his unfinished commentary, covering only Books III-V,[2] remaining in manuscript.[3] Copernicus had put the stationary sun in the center of the universe; this heliocentrism was rejected by Reinhold, who placed the earth there. But Reinhold's rejection of Copernican heliocentrism was by no means a mere reaffirmation of the ancient geocentric astronomy. For Reinhold formulated his own new hypotheses (*hypotheses novas*), in which an outer planet's stations and retrogradations were produced, not by the planet's motion on a Ptolemaic epicycle, but by the sun moving in an orbit centered at the center of the universe. Thus, at fol. 233r[4] in his commentary on the *Revolutions*, V, 14,□ Reinhold reproduced a diagram in which 53
Copernicus had denoted the stationary sun in the center of the universe by E, while S marked the momentary place

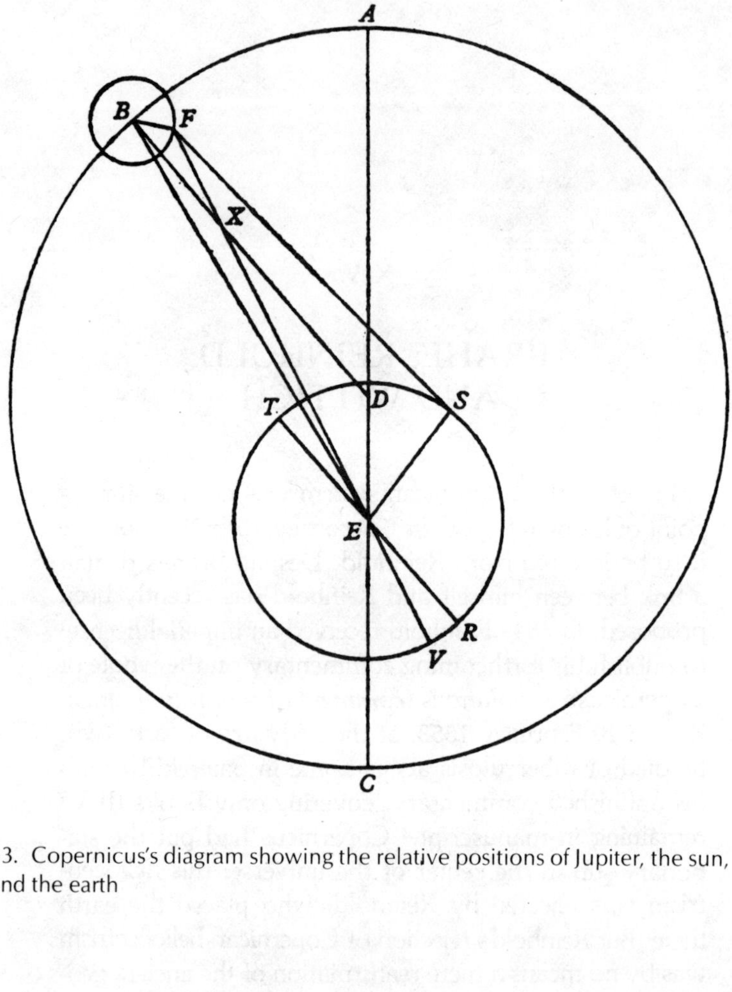

53. Copernicus's diagram showing the relative positions of Jupiter, the sun, and the earth

of the earth as it moved around the sun in E. These two letters, E and S, were interchanged by Reinhold, who wrote in the text of his commentary:

> Let S be the earth's place for Copernicus,[5] but for me the sun's place.

Then, deleting these last four Latin words, Reinhold wrote more amply in the left margin opposite them:

> According to my new hypotheses, the sun's place would be S, as against[6] E, the center of the universe.

What this interchange implied was made explicit on the other side of fol. 233. There Reinhold's commentary says that his sun, moving in an orbit centered at the center of the universe, accounted for Jupiter's stations and retrogradations by replacing Ptolemy's epicycle and Copernicus's Grand Orb.[7] In short, toward the end of his prematurely curtailed life Reinhold began to work out the basic idea of Tycho's hypotheses.

When Reinhold died, Brahe was only seven years old; there was no personal contact between them. But twenty-two years later, when Brahe was returning from the coronation of Rudolph II on 1 November 1575 at Regensburg, he traveled northwest to Saalfeld, where he visited Erasmus Reinhold, Jr., M.D. The doctor and the astronomer talked about the manuscripts that had been left by the doctor's father, and Brahe was shown, among other things, the manuscript of the *Prussian Tables*. Although the conversation was brief (*tam brevi tempore*), Brahe learned from their friendly talk (*ex solo familiari colloquio*) that Reinhold Jr. had little time for astronomy, since he had to support his family by his medical practice. In fact, apart from correspondence concerning the longitudes of Frombork and

Koenigsberg, and a discussion of the 1572 nova, which he issued with his astrological prognostication for 1574, his relevant publications consisted of annual predictions for 1568-1575, designed to produce a personal income.[8] Reinhold Sr.'s commentary on Copernicus is not mentioned by Brahe in his account of his conversation with Reinhold Jr.,[9] nor is there any indication that the latter was aware of the new proto-Tychonic hypotheses recorded in his father's commentary.

That unfinished and unsigned work was mistakenly regarded for about three and a half centuries as lost. When it was finally unearthed shortly before the beginning of the present century by two outstanding researchers,[10] neither of them noticed its proto-Tychonic tendency. That was disclosed for the first time in 1957 to an international congress, whose proceedings were published in 1960.[11] Hence, for over four hundred years Reinhold's step in the Tychonic direction remained unknown, even to his colleagues and successors in the University of Wittenberg, which Brahe visited on four occasions.[12] Accordingly, there is no historical foundation for the recent guess "that Tycho's own cosmological views grew from seeds planted at Wittenberg."[13]

The gravity of the error linking Brahe's hypotheses with Wittenberg and Reinhold was intensified by the recent misattribution to Brahe of an extensively annotated copy of the first edition of Copernicus's *Revolutions* in the Vatican Library, erroneously described as "probably the most important Tycho manuscript in existence."[14] Bound in at the end of this Vatican copy are thirty manuscript pages. A comparison of the handwriting on these pages with fac-
54, 55 similes of Tycho's authentic handwriting[15]□□ establishes beyond any doubt that the anonymous writer of the manuscript pages in the Vatican copy was not Tycho Brahe.

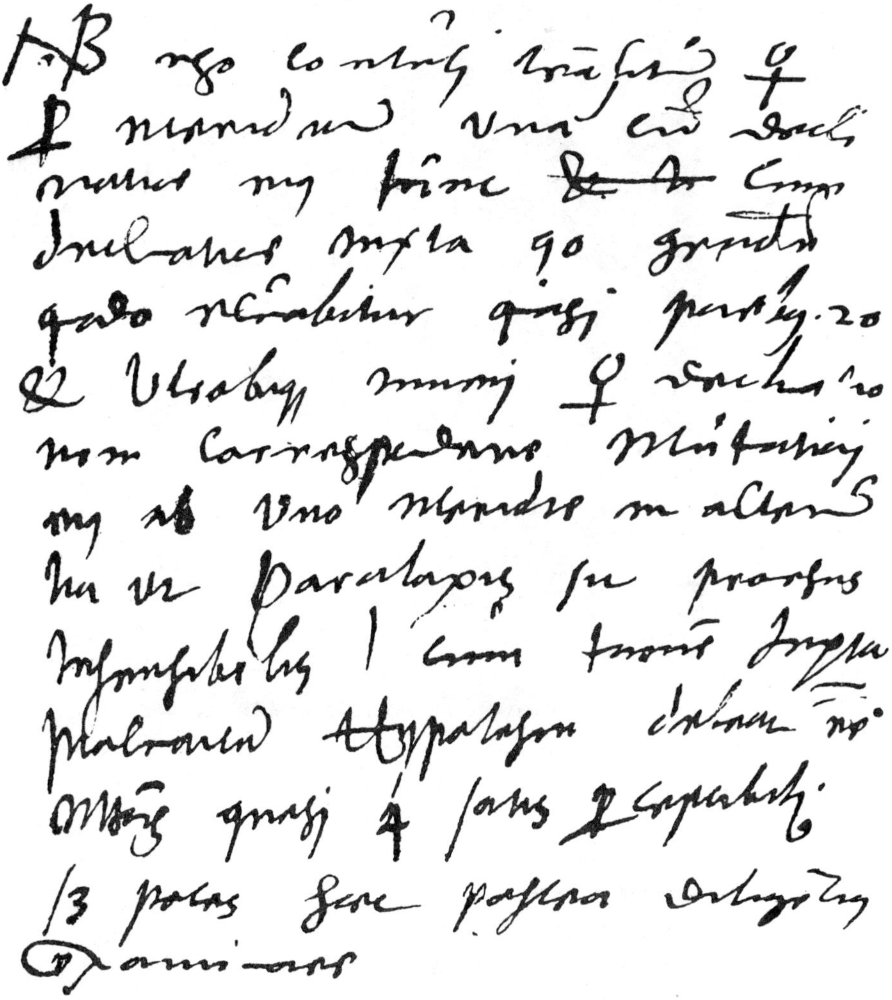

54. Brahe's observation of Venus, 3 March 1590

The handwriting in the Vatican copy of the first edition of Copernicus's *Revolutions*, on the other hand, is identical with the annotator's handwriting in a Prague copy of the second edition of Copernicus's *Revolutions*. A facsimile of this Prague copy was published in 1971 by Zdeněk Horský, who main-

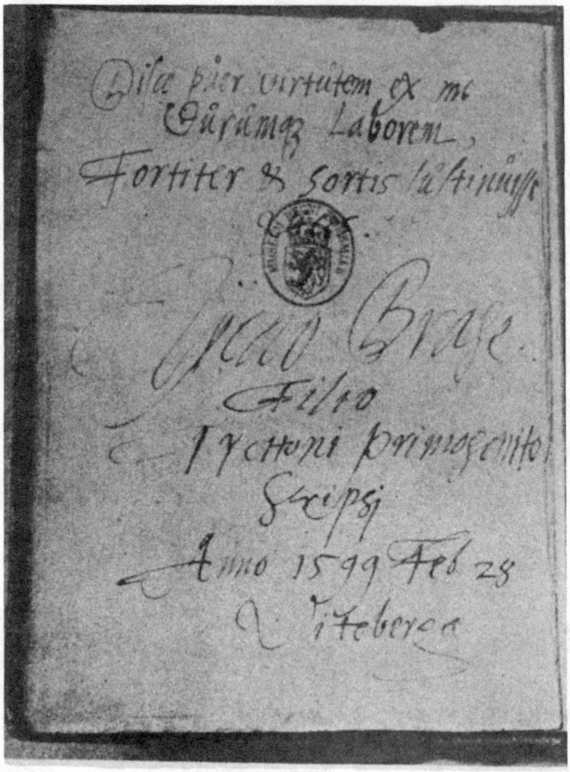

55. Brahe's entry in the album of his eldest son, Tycho Jr., on 28 February 1599 in Wittenberg

tained that the annotator was Brahe.[16] Limiting the possible alternative annotators to four astronomers, Robert S. Westman stated:

> On the basis of a handwriting comparison, which I have undertaken, between works and letters of the above mentioned writers and DR Prague [= the Prague facsimile], there can be no doubt that Horský's identification is correct.[17]

The annotator's handwriting was not compared with Brahe's by Westman. His limited comparison showed that the annotator was not one of four astronomers other than Brahe. How could these four eliminations

56. Duncan Liddel (1561-1613), "the first in Germany to teach the theories of the heavenly motions according to the hypotheses of Ptolemy and Copernicus at the same time"

prove that Brahe was the annotator? He was in fact a fifth astronomer.

In a personal letter dated 31 July 1980 Professor Owen Gingerich identified the Vatican-Prague annotator as Paul Wittich without furnishing any evidence. It so happens that in 1582-1584 Wittich gave private instruction to Duncan Liddel□ 56
(1561-1613), who later became the "first in Germany to teach the theories of the heavenly motions according to the hypothesis of Ptolemy and Copernicus at the same time."[18] In the winter semester of 1579, Liddel, a Scot from Aberdeen, had enrolled in the University of Frankfurt on the Oder,[19]□ where 57
his fellow-countryman John Craig (?-1620) was then teaching. Craig had previously studied Copernicus's astronomy with Wittich, whose annotations he reproduced in his own copy of the second edition of the *Revolutions*, which is now in the library of the University of Edinburgh. In an annotation where

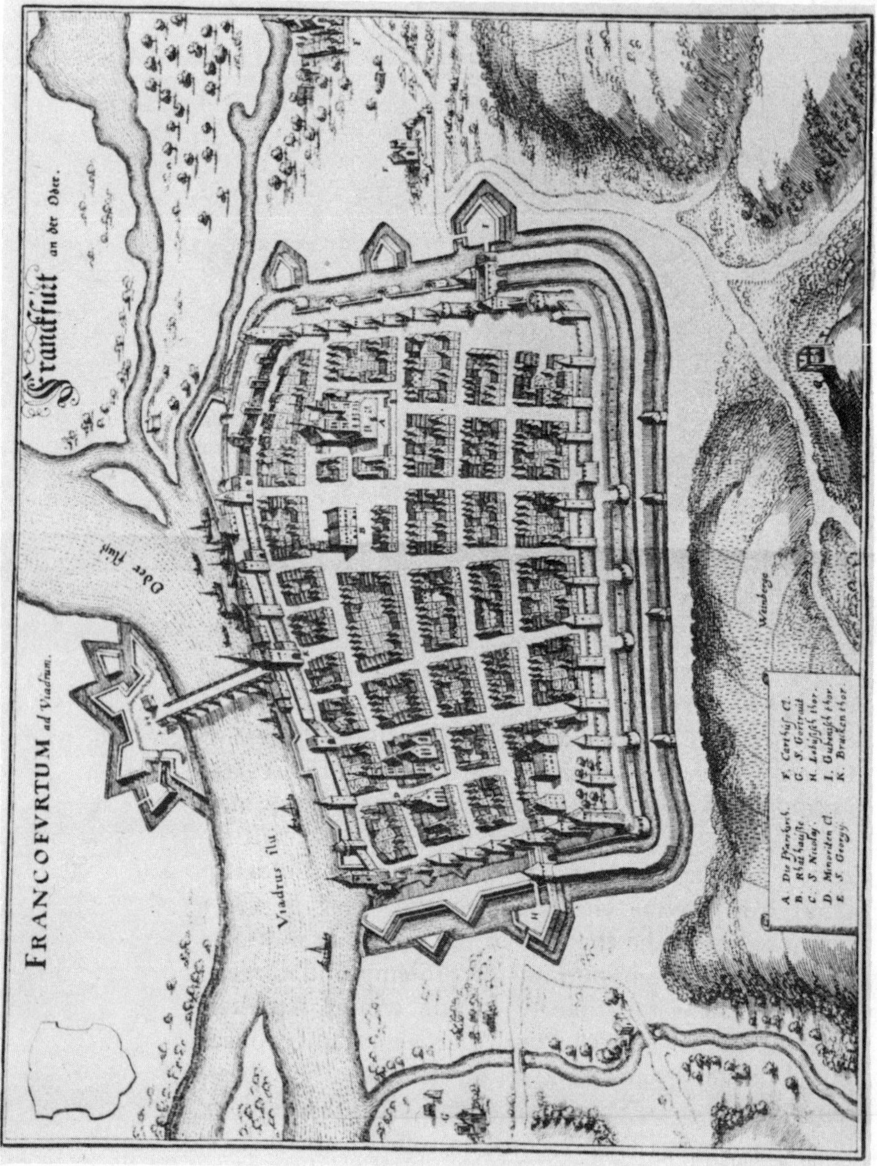

57. Frankfurt an der Oder, where Duncan Liddel enrolled at the local university in the winter semester of 1579

Wittich had written that something was "found by me," Craig shifted to "found by M[aster] Witt[ich]."[20] The "first principles" of Copernicanism were imparted by Craig to Liddel, who "learned more completely from Wittich...about Copernicus's innovative hypotheses."[21]

Liddel interleaved his copy of the second edition of Copernicus's *Revolutions*, which is preserved in the Aberdeen University Library.[22] A facsimile of the interleaf facing folio 9v in Liddel's copy may be conveniently compared with a facsimile of folio 9v in Wittich's copy.[23] In the left margin Wittich had tabulated the planets' periodic motions, and his table was repeated by Liddel, with only two variants. First, as regards the earth, in the column for the years, Wittich had mistakenly written 365, which he struck out and transferred to the column for the days, while leaving only a smudge in the column for the years. Wittich had evidently made this scribal correction before the arrival of Liddel, who has a zero in the years column for the earth. A second telltale sign of Liddel's dependence on Wittich concerns the moon, where Wittich had 0 27 19 18, and Liddel interchanged the last two columns: 0 27 18 19.

The rectification of a bad blunder committed by Copernicus concerning Venus's sidereal period throws further light on the time when Wittich wrote his annotations. Liddel left undisturbed not only *Venus nonimestris* in Copernicus's famous diagram of the cosmos, but also Copernicus's *Venus nono mense reducitur* (Venus returns in nine months)[24] three lines above the diagram. After Liddel's departure, however, Wittich changed *nono* to *octavo*, and *nonimestris* to *octimestris*, since his marginal table gave only 224 (plus a fraction) days for Venus's sidereal period. By the same token, since his table showed 87 (plus more than 1/2) days for Mercury, he altered Copernicus's text by adding *et octo* (and eight) to *octuaginta* (eighty). These alterations were made by Wittich after the departure of Liddel, whose copy does not show them. Evidently Wittich continued to annotate his copy of Copernicus after Liddel had left.

No clue to Wittich's identity has been found either in his copy of the first edition of Copernicus's *Revolutions* (Ottoboniano Latino #1902) or in his copy of the second edition (Prague facsimile). Nevertheless, the handwriting in these two copies can be compared with an authenticated sample of Wittich's handwriting.

Wittich was one of Brahe's assistants while the comet of 1580 was visible. During Brahe's absence from his observatory, the observations of 21, 22, and 26 October 1580 were recorded by Wittich, who remained at the observatory. This handwriting was certified as his by a fellow-townsman and fellow-astronomer, Jacob Monaw of Wrocław.

> These pages marked with the letters A. B. C. D. E., I recognize to have been written by the hand of Paul Wittich, of blessed memory, which is very well known to me, and I so testify with this handwritten note which I left at Prague with the magnificent and most noble lord Tycho Brahe on 23 October 1600.
>
> Jacob Monaw[25]
> 58 with my own hand□

A small specimen of these cometary observations in Wittich's handwriting was reproduced in Brahe's collected works.[26] The words *Occasus*, *aquila*, and *Informis*, as written by Wittich, when compared with the same words written by Brahe, show marked differences.[27] On the other hand, many words on pages A.B.C.D.E., of which a photocopy was kindly supplied by the Royal Library in Copenhagen, match the corresponding words in the Prague facsimile. Some examples follow:

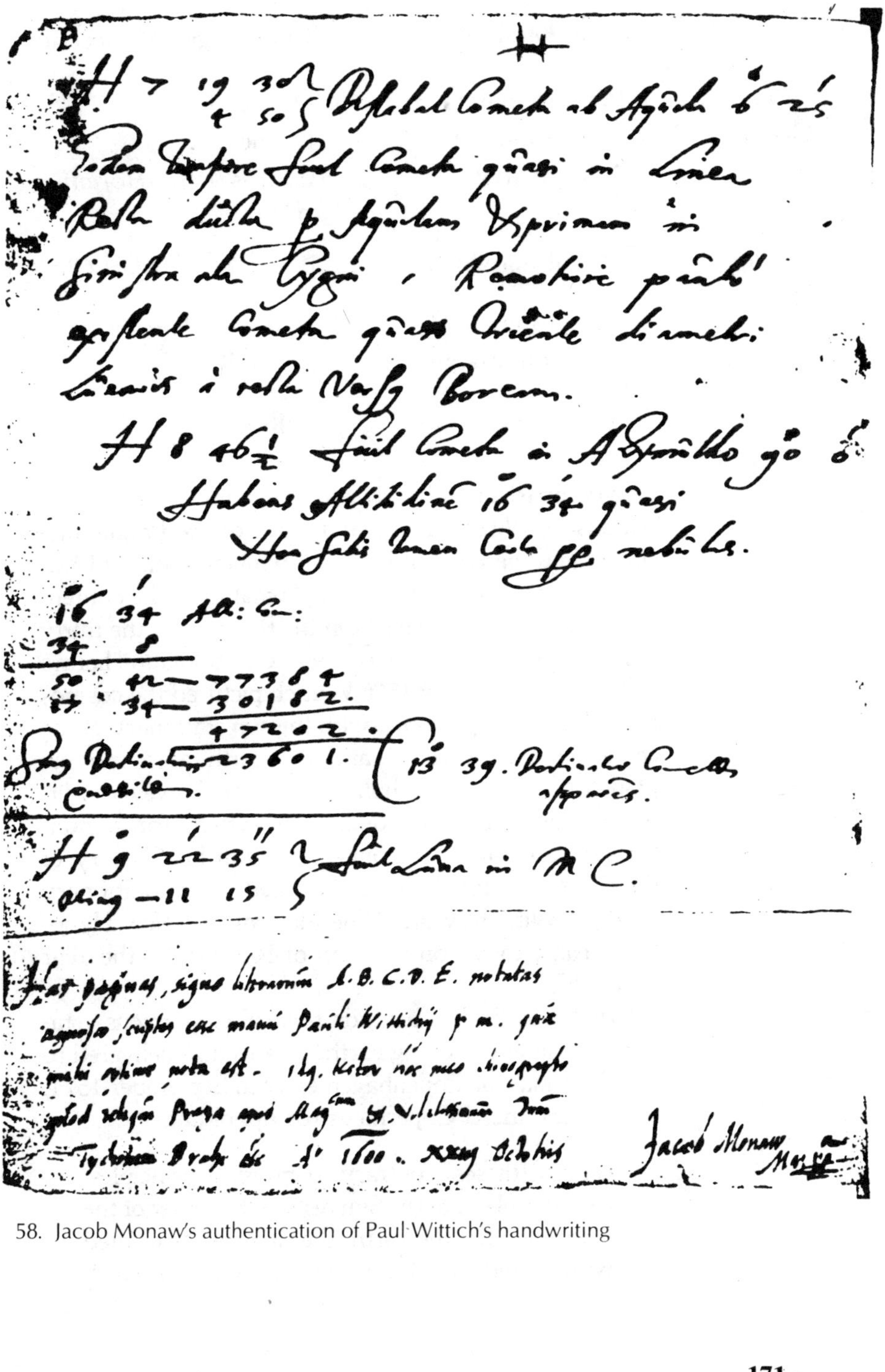

58. Jacob Monaw's authentication of Paul Wittich's handwriting

	Prague Facsimile	**Copenhagen Manuscript**
Distantia	fol.8r/top margin/3	D/lines 1,7
Occasu	10r/right margin/2	D/line 2
Horae	38v/left margin	C/lines 9, 13 (*Horam, Hora*)
M[edium] C[oeli]	40r/right margin/6	B/line 7 (*M[edio] C[oeli]*)
Lineas Rectas	68r/right margin/4	D/line 6 (*Lineam Rectam*)
extrema	68v/bottom margin/ last line	A/last line
Vero	113r/right margin/5	C/line 5

This comparison of handwritings eliminates Brahe, and establishes Wittich as the annotator of the Prague facsimile, and therefore also of Ottoboniano Latino #1902.

Apart from the handwritings, what does the content of the annotations reveal? On the first two of the thirty manuscript pages bound into Ottoboniano Latino #1902, on 27 January 1578 Wittich pictured the cosmos according to Copernicus, with the sun stationary at the center of the universe, and the earth as a moving
59 planet.[28]□ Two and a half weeks later, however, Wittich abandoned this Copernican system for a non-Copernican stance. In connection with his "Theory of the Three Outer Planets Adjusted to a Stationary Earth,"[29] Wittich wrote: "The Idea for this New Hypothesis came to me on the 13th of February in the Year
60 1578."[30]□

What was Brahe's attitude toward Copernicus's stationary sun and moving earth? In a lecture delivered to the University of Copenhagen early in September 1574, Brahe denounced Copernicus for upholding

> certain [theses] contrary to physical principles, for example, that the Sun rests at the center of the Universe, that the Earth, the elements associated with it, and the Moon, move around the Sun.[31]

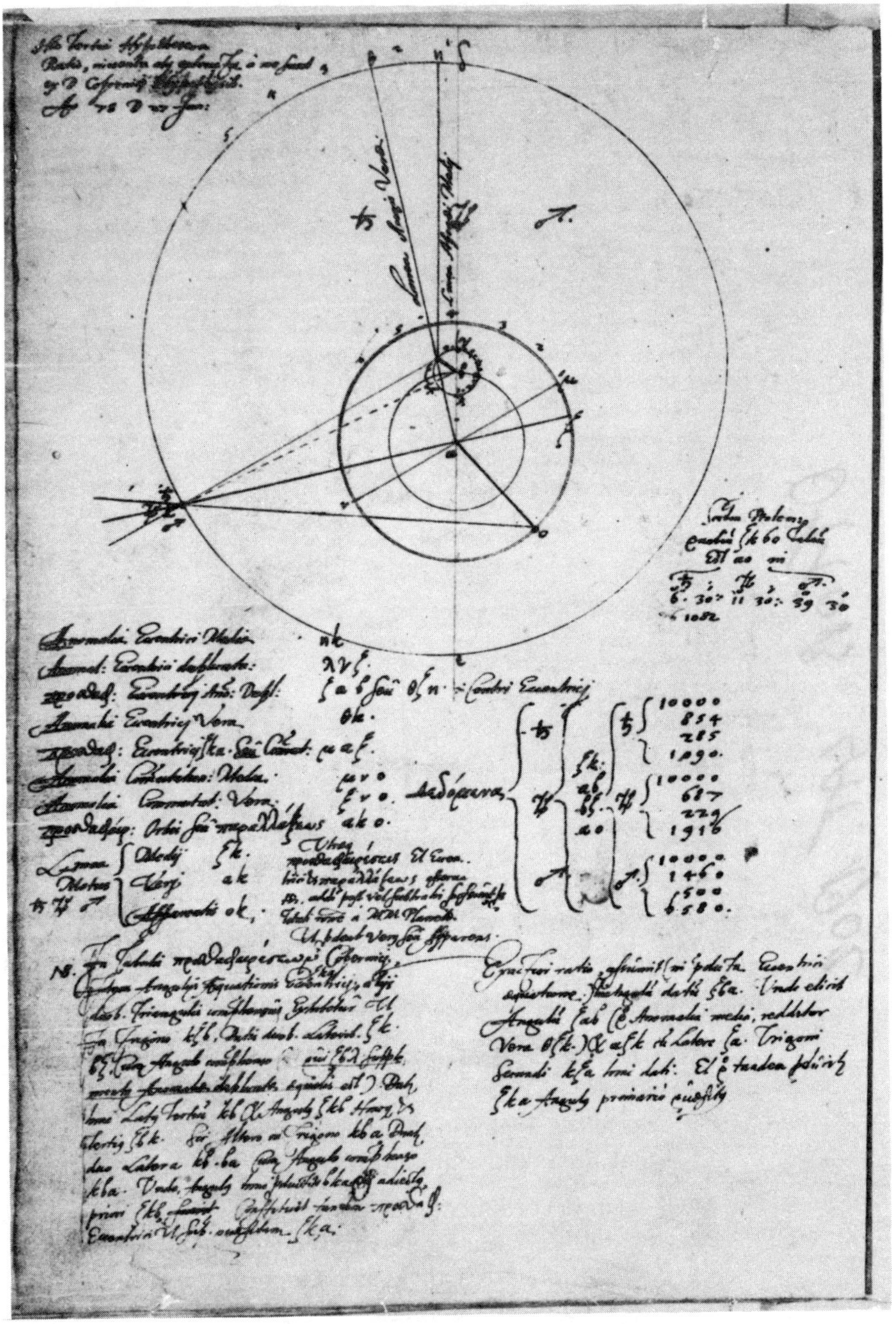

59. Paul Wittich's diagram, dated 27 January 1578

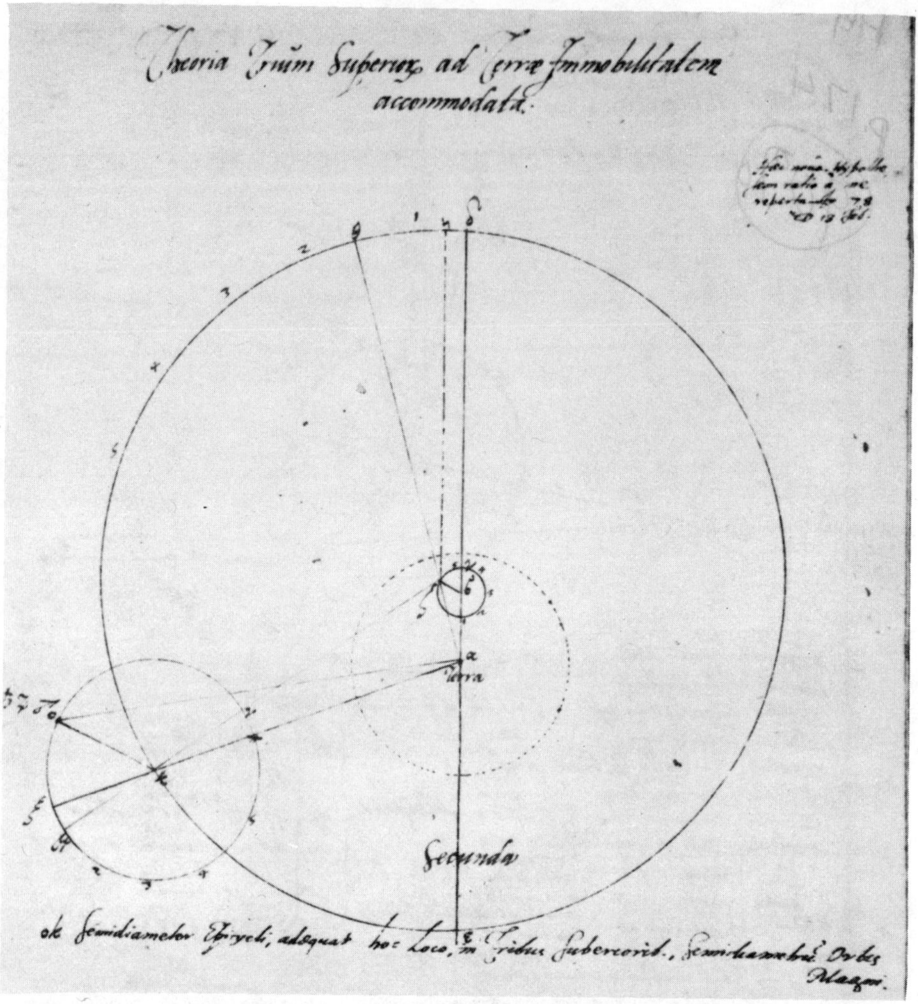

60. Paul Wittich's diagram, dated 13 February 1578

Speaking again on the following day, Tycho explained that he would expound planetary theory succinctly

> in accordance with Copernicus's thinking and tables, but referring everything to the stationary earth, which Copernicus had imagined to be moving.[32]

Resting on faith in the Bible and physical (better called "metaphysical") principles, Brahe's earth remained stationary throughout his life. His allegiance never swerved, as did Wittich's in 1578, between 27 January and 13 February. Before abandoning Copernicanism, Wittich had written at the top of the right margin of folio 10r, Ottoboniano Latino #1902:

> The evidence of the planets in particular conforms exactly to the earth's mobility, and in this way it is confirmed that Copernicus's hypotheses were assumed correctly.[33]

Evidently Wittich wrote this annotation before 13 February 1578. But thereafter, when he returned to an immobile earth, he made it the center around which the three outer planets (Saturn, Jupiter, and Mars) revolved.[34] In this respect Wittich differed from Brahe, whose outer planets revolved around the sun. When Brahe traced his intellectual development from his acquiescing youth until he rejected the contemporary competing cosmologies, at that time he asked himself what

> if the sun were established as the center of the five planets, and nevertheless revolved once a year around the earth, at rest in the center of the universe.[35]

From the very beginning of his independent swing away from the prevailing conventional wisdom, Brahe centered the planets on the sun. From this conception, as previously expounded by Copernicus, Brahe never deviated throughout the rest of his life.

Brahe's thinking, like his handwriting, was different from Wittich's. The time when Brahe first conceived his Tychonic system (1583) likewise differs from the time when Wittich first broke away from Copernicanism (1578). "Those five years were an important time of maturing" for Brahe, concluded Gingerich,[36] while he was misled by his own misattribution of Ottoboniano Latino #1902 to Tycho. By the same token Westman insisted that

> We now have dramatic evidence from the manuscript notes bound into the back of DR Vatican [=Ottoboniano Latino #1902], that the first step toward his [Brahe's] final system was initially formulated, on paper at least, on 17 February 1578.[37]

Brahe himself, however, related that

> finally almost against hope[38] I realized by what arrangement the order of the heavenly revolutions comes to be disposed most appropriately.[39]

Brahe dated this realization in 1583, without any first step or initial formulation in 1578.

The misidentification of Brahe as the annotator of Ottoboniano Latino #1902 was based on the previous misidentification of Brahe as the annotator of the Prague facsimile. On its title page is written: "Property of the Imperial College of the Society of Jesus in Prague, in the year 1642" (*Collegii Caesarei Societatis Jesu Pragae Anno 1642*). The same hand added: "From the Library and Scrutiny of Tycho" (*Ex*
61 *Bibliotheca et Recognitione Tichoniana*).□ On the flyleaf preceding the title page a different hand pointed out: "Observe: There are present marginal notes written by Tycho Brahe's own hand" (*NB Insunt notae marginales manu Tychonis Brahe propria inscriptae*).

This volume was donated to the Prague Jesuits in 1642 by the heirs of Tycho Brahe.[40] Ever since his death on 24 October 1601 they had been struggling ineffectually to obtain from the imperial treasury the sums owed to them for what Tycho Brahe, the Imperial Mathematician, had left behind. By contrast with his observational instruments and personal manuscripts, his library had passed into the possession of his younger son, George Brahe (1583-1640).

NICOLAI
COPERNICI TO-
RINENSIS DE REVOLVTIONI-
bus orbium cœlestium,
Libri VI.

IN QVIBVS STELLARVM ET FI-
XARVM ET ERRATICARVM MOTVS, EX VETE-
ribus atque recentibus obseruationibus, restituit hic autor.
Præterea tabulas expeditas luculentasque addidit, ex qui-
bus eosdem motus ad quoduis tempus Mathe-
matum studiosus facillime calcu-
lare poterit.

ITEM, DE LIBRIS REVOLVTIONVM NICOLAI
Copernici Narratio prima, per M. Georgium Ioachi-
mum Rheticum ad D. Ioan. Schone-
rum scripta.

Collegij Cæsa= rei Socti IESV
Pragæ. A°. 1642.

Ex Bibliothecâ
et Recognitione
Tichonianâ.

REGIÆ. BIBLIOTH: ACAD: PRAGEN:

Cum Gratia & Priuilegio Cæs. Maiest.
BASILEAE, EX OFFICINA
HENRICPETRINA.

61. Title Page of the copy of Copernicus's *Revolutions*, 2nd ed. Basel, 1566, that belonged to Paul Wittich and was acquired by Tycho Brahe

On 16 November 1624 Kepler, who had formerly been Tycho Brahe's principal assistant, recommended to George Brahe that "a careful catalog should be compiled of everything in the way of books and manuscripts still surviving from Tycho's library."[41] Kepler's advice was not heeded, and no such Tycho catalog was ever prepared. But two years after George Brahe's death, the heirs being divided between those who left because they remained faithful to Protestantism and those who converted to Catholicism, the latter group, to curry favor with the imperial authorities, made various donations to Catholic orders, including Tycho Brahe's copy of the second edition (Basel, 1566) of Copernicus's *Revolutions*, which went to the Prague Jesuits. Knowing that the book had once belonged to Tycho Brahe, and seeing that it was heavily annotated, they identified the unnamed annotator as Tycho himself. Had they compared the annotator's handwriting with the numerous examples of Tycho's authentic handwriting in their possession and at their disposal, they would have seen at a glance that the annotator was not Tycho. But this comparison was not instituted by the Jesuits, whose misattribution of the annotations to Tycho certainly enhanced the value of the volume to undiscriminating eyes.

With regard to this volume, the distinguished biographer of Tycho Brahe and editor of his correspondence and cometary observations, Frederik Reinholdt Friis (1836-1910), said:

> This copy is completely provided on nearly every page with added notes and corrections, but these could not be additions by the astronomer [Tycho Brahe], as has been assumed heretofore.[42]

This assumption, accepting the 1642 Jesuit attribution, had been made by the historian of the Prague University library, Joseph Adolph Hanslik (1785-1859).[43] Friis's rejection of the attribution of the Prague annotations to Tycho was ignored by a long string of students who accepted the Jesuits' claim,[44] culminating in the Prague facsimile, which maintained:

> Tycho Brahe is really the author of these notes.... [W]e have the possibility of judging the handwriting.... [E]ssentially it is like the writing in well-known and undoubted relics of Tycho's manuscripts.[45]

But the Prague facsimile did not document this asserted essential similarity by presenting handwriting samples of Tycho and the annotator side by side.

The annotator's handwriting has already been shown to be Wittich's. How was his heavily annotated copy of the second edition of Copernicus's *Revolutions* acquired by Brahe? On 24 March 1598 Tycho wrote to a favorite pupil:

> A few days ago my dear friend Jacob Monaw of Wrocław wrote to me that at the end of last year [1597] you came to Wrocław ... In the same letter Monaw reported that he arranged to have you introduced to the sister of Wittich, of blessed memory [†9 January 1586],[46] where you examined all his books. I therefore ask you to inform me about them, what they were and of what sort, especially the manuscripts, and whether she wants to sell them and at what price.[47]

Nearly two years later Monaw (1546-1603) wrote to Brahe on 14 March 1600:

> As far as Wittich's books are concerned, I want you to know that at the time when your letter was delivered here, Paul Wittich's sister, already advanced in age, celebrated her second marriage, of which the result was that the newlywed died after sixty days. She left one son as her heir, for whom legitimate guardians have

> not yet been appointed. When this is taken care of, I shall see whether anything can be done with them.[48]

On 23 October 1600 Monaw was with Brahe in Prague, where he identified the handwriting of the cometary observations of 21, 22 and 26 October 1580 as Wittich's.[49] On that occasion Monaw delivered Wittich's copy of the second edition of Copernicus's *Revolutions* to Brahe, who was not the original owner of the book, but the second owner. After the death of Wittich's sister, an unidentified male—perhaps a guardian of her son—wrote at the top of the flyleaf preceding the title page several entries in two columns. The left-hand column concerns his career:

> At the beginning of the month of March in both
> 1568 into the senate Rahvitz
> 1588 to the magistracy

In the right-hand column he noted that in

> [15]66 in October I married my first wife
> [15]90 in the month of October she died
> [15]93 in the month of October I married my second wife

The foregoing entries dovetail with Monaw's purchase of Wittich's copy of the second edition of Copernicus's *Revolutions* from the guardians of Wittich's nephew for Brahe, who acquired the book only a year before his death. Brahe was therefore the second owner of the book. The Jesuits' explanation on its title page that it came to them from Tycho's library (*Ex Bibliotheca... Tichoniana*) does not mean that he was its "original owner," an erroneous inference drawn by the editor of the Prague facsimile[50] and by Westman.[51] Brahe was its owner, but not its annotator, and its annotations help us understand Wittich's reactions to Copernicanism, not Brahe's.

A Leningrad copy of the first edition of Copernicus's *Revolutions* has numerous annotations, some of which are marked by the letters "R" or "Re," referring to Erasmus Reinhold. These were recently described as having been written by Reinhold himself.[52] Other annotations beginning as follows: "I (Tycho Brahe) ..." were similarly described as having been written by Brahe himself. The book itself was said to have been originally owned by Erasmus Reinhold, and handed by his heir in Saalfeld in 1575 to Brahe, who thereby became its second owner and second annotator.

Even more recently,[53] the Leningrad Brahe annotations were correctly described as being quotations from his printed works by an unidentified annotator. By the same token, the Leningrad Reinhold annotations were identified as having been copied from the annotations in a Liège copy of Copernicus's *Revolutions,* the Liège annotations having been previously copied from Erasmus Reinhold's own copy of the first edition of Copernicus's *Revolutions,* which is now in Edinburgh. Clearly, then, the Leningrad copy of the first edition of Copernicus's *Revolutions* was not originally owned by Erasmus Reinhold, nor did it pass to Tycho Brahe as its second owner nor, after his death, to Kepler, to whom some Leningrad annotations were ascribed.

XV

URSUS'S MISUNDERSTANDING OF COPERNICUS

XV

URSUS'S MISUNDERSTANDING OF COPERNICUS

As Kepler reported to Herwart in his letter of 20/30 May 1599, whereas Brahe insisted that the departures of his own hypotheses from Copernicus's were all of his own contrivance,

> In opposition Ursus [contends] that his own hypotheses as well as Tycho's were taken from the hypotheses published long ago by Apollonius of Perga about the time of Christ.[1]

Kepler simply repeated the misdating of Apollonius by Ursus, who said that the great Greek scientist "flourished a little after the birth and crucifixion of Christ."[2] While even today very little is known about Apollonius's life, it is now certain that he flourished about 200 B.C.

> As the basis of this contention of his, Ursus cites[3] some passages in Copernicus, where a part of Tycho's hypothesis is formulated explicitly by Copernicus himself, and a part is ascribed to Apollonius of Perga. But in those passages Copernicus does not in the least say what Ursus claims. For Copernicus neither expounds Tycho's hypothesis (Ursus misunder-

stands the exposition) nor does Copernicus ascribe the hypothesis to Apollonius of Perga. Ursus admits that

(1) he took his hypothesis from someone else;

(2) he found it formulated in Copernicus and attributed to Apollonius;

(3) it is the same as Tycho's.

Ursus therefore concedes that he copied it from somebody who says the same thing as Tycho.

Observe that whoever showed his own hypotheses to Ursus (except for a slight detail that is easily changed) hypothesizes in exactly the same way as Tycho. But who is he? According to Ursus, he is Copernicus, and Apollonius in Copernicus, and nobody else. Therefore Ursus's hypotheses were originated by nobody but Apollonius in Copernicus or Brahe. But I say that the originator of Ursus's hypotheses is neither Apollonius nor Copernicus. Therefore only Tycho is. Apart from him, nobody completely conducted Ursus to his hypotheses. The basis of the case is that we should have Copernicus's authentic thinking. The rest was thought up by Ursus himself, according to his own admission. In the *Revolutions*, III, 25, Ursus thinks that Tycho's hypotheses are expounded by Copernicus.[4] To be sure, Copernicus concedes that some of the motions which he assigned to the earth can be transferred to the sun. But he does not make that concession with regard to the annual revolution.[5] Nor does he there discuss the motions of the five primary planets. They are not the subject of Book [III], which is exclusively concerned with the motion of the sun (or of the earth) without regard to the motions of the other heavenly bodies.

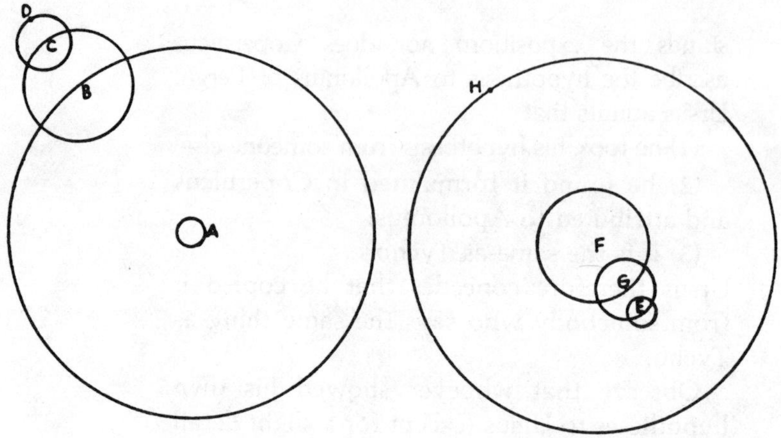

Haec est hypothesis Copernicj circa unum Orbem Terrae vel Solis.

Haec est mutatio, quam lib:3. C:25, etiam possibilem ponit, et in dubio relinquit.

62. Kepler's diagrams illustrating Copernicus's explanation of the displacement of the solar apogee

To clarify the matter, I shall draw two
62 diagrams□ setting forth the thinking of Copernicus. In the first diagram, A is the center of the universe as well as of the body of the sun. B is the center of the epicycle which dispenses with an eccentric. (Copernicus produces the eccentric effect by combining an epicycle with the Grand Orb, but he himself says that [the two models] are equivalent).[6]

To account for the difference in the length of the four seasons of the year, ancient astronomers had invoked the principle of eccentricity. The moving body (in their opinion, the sun) circled around the stationary body (in their opinion, the earth). This was located not in, but outside, the center of the circle. This eccentric motion made the four seasons unequal in duration. Copernicus held the sun stationary in A, the center of the universe. He made the earth revolve once a year around the sun in what he called the

Grand Orb (*orbis magnus*). But instead of making the Grand Orb eccentric, he produced the equivalent of the eccentric effect by means of the epicyclic device. B, the center of the epicycle, revolves uniformly around the circumference of a circle concentric with the center of the universe, which in the first diagram is identical with the center of the body of the sun.

> In the course of a year B travels uniformly around A. The variation in the eccentricity is supplied by C, the epicyclet's center. C revolves around B, likewise in an annual motion [but] in the opposite direction. D is the earth, which is carried around C in 3,434 years.[7]

Because the eccentricity varies, Copernicus introduces a second and smaller epicyclet, which carries the earth D around on its circumference in 3,434 years. The epicyclet's center C revolves around the circumference of the larger epicycle, whose center B in turn revolves annually around the Grand Orb.

> In the second diagram, F is the center of the universe as well as of the motion of the earth H. It revolves in an annual motion that in itself is uniform. E is the center of the body of the sun, which revolves around center G in 3,434 years. G, the center of the epicycle which carries the sun E, produces the displacement of the solar apogee. For in relation to the fixed stars G revolves around F in 17,108 years, according to Copernicus and the *Prussian* [*Tables*].[8]

The "solar apogee" was the pre-Copernican term for the point where the distance between the sun and the earth reaches its maximum. This apogeal point undergoes a very slow displacement with respect to the stars. The mean annual displacement given by Copernicus's *Revolutions* was 24″ 20‴ 14⁗ = 54,000 years for a complete circuit.[9] The displacement of the solar apogee was not discussed in Reinhold's *Prussian Tables*.

> Therefore the sun will move from its place in two motions, but very slowly and not far. For, the circlets [EG, FG] are quite tiny in comparison with the circle on which the earth runs, in both diagrams.[10]

Kepler's diagrams are not drawn to scale: AB in the first diagram, and FH in the second diagram, should be very much bigger than BC and FG, respectively.

> Either because he does not understand or because he is foolish (Ursus expected that nobody would comprehend these models), he thinks that Copernicus is talking about a solar motion which would be similar to the Copernican annual motion of the earth, and would have some effect on the parallaxes of the five planets. For these two [motions, centered on F and G], which are assigned to the sun by Copernicus in his second treatment, are ignored in his discussion of the other planets, whether [these two motions] are attributed to the earth or to the sun. Yet analysis does require the intrusion by them of that slight effect which Tycho seems to detect in his observations. So much for the first treatment.
>
> In the remaining passages cited from Copernicus, V, 3 and 35, Ursus's case is very much worse. Copernicus took his reference to Apollonius of Perga and to Apollonius's theorem from Ptolemy.[11]

In the *Revolutions*, V, 3, Copernicus emphasized a defect in Apollonius's discussion of the planets' stationary points, while in V, 35, he incorporated Apollonius's theorem in his own treatment of that subject.[12]

> I am surprised that Ursus did not read this material in Ptolemy.[13]

Apollonius's theorem has survived only because it was incorporated by Ptolemy in his *Syntaxis*, XII, 1. But it so happens that Copernicus did not indicate where he had found Apollonius's theorem. Ursus's unfamiliarity with Ptolemy as the repository of Apollonius's theorem implies that Ursus was unfamiliar with the *Syntaxis*, that grand summation of ancient Greek astronomy.

> Apollonius's meaning is almost entirely different, since he is not engaged in considering the whole five-planet system, whose center is located in the body of the sun. That is what is done by Tycho, Ursus, Copernicus, and the ancients [who accepted heliocentricity. Apollonius's interest], on the other hand, is solely to declare what ratio to its deferent each planet's epicycle must have by itself, as well as the ratio of epicycle and deferent to that planet's nonuniform retrograde motion and to its uniform periodic motion, so that its station and retrogradation may follow from these ratios.[14]

As observed, a planet moves eastward most of the time until it reaches a stationary point. There it reverses its direction and enters its retrogradation. This retrograde motion westward continues until the planet reaches its second stationary point, where it reverses its direction again and resumes its eastward course.□ 63

> Thus the very defect in Apollonius's hypotheses was his belief that every planet has only one nonuniformity, which is regulated by Ptolemy through an epicycle. Apollonius did not know that the epicycle's center also advances nonuniformly or, according to Ptolemy, on an eccentric.[15]

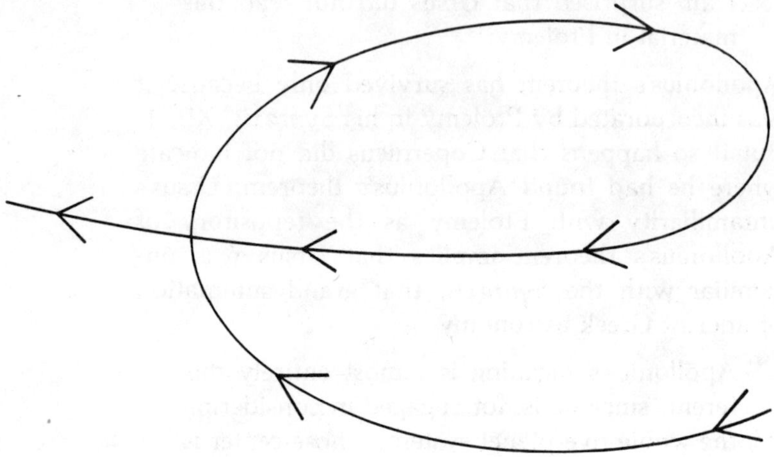

63. Planet's loop

In the margin Kepler remarked:

> Ptolemy praises Apollonius, not for the substance of his hypotheses, but for the ingenuity of his admittedly highly elegant proof. See Reinhold on Peurbach's *Theory*, in the chapter on the stations.[16]

Erasmus Reinhold, Sr.'s *Commentary on Peurbach's New Theory of the Planets* (Wittenberg, 1542), Part 2, treated planetary phenomena, beginning with the stations. Perhaps that is why Kepler called it the "chapter on the stations." At sig. Rlv (misprinted K in the 1542 edition) Reinhold said that the second portion of Apollonius's theorem "is not devoid of ingenuity and earns more admiration."

> The foregoing is the meaning of the [Copernican] passages cited [by Ursus], as all specialists will agree. Ursus, however, is either blind or cunning. By parenthetically interpolating the word "movable," Ursus wishes to convince [us]

> that Apollonius, or Copernicus in his stead, is talking about the common motion of all five planets because their center, the sun, revolves in an annual motion. This is the motion proclaimed by Tycho's hypotheses [as the sun's] and attributed to the earth by Copernicus. And this is the nub of the case.[17]

Copernicus's sun is stationary. By interpolating the word "movable," and attaching it to the sun, Ursus surreptitiously transmutes Copernicus's stationary sun into Brahe's movable sun as the center of the five planets, and thereby twists Copernicus's non-Tychonic system in the Tychonic direction.

XVI

URSUS'S ADMISSION OF HIS INTELLECTUAL THEFT

XVI

URSUS'S ADMISSION OF HIS INTELLECTUAL THEFT

Having convicted Ursus of misrepresenting the sun in Copernicus's system, in his letter of 20/30 May 1599 to Herwart, Kepler proceeded to emphasize Ursus's own admission that he was a thief. What he stole was not anything material. But it was intellectual.

> In the mind of anybody who weighs these considerations carefully, at once a suspicion arises spontaneously from all the circumstances. Ursus admits that he is guilty of an intellectual theft: in Magdeburg he made public Tycho's theory about the structure of the universe, but [he put it] alongside his own. That, naturally, was born of a mother. She is a non-person, as we learned from our previous investigation.[1]

Brahe published his letter to Rothmann of 21 February 1589 in his *Astronomical Letters* (Uraniburg, 1596), and it was promptly reprinted by Ursus in his own *Astronomical Hypotheses* (Prague, 1597) for purposes of rebuttal. Numbering Brahe's expressions to which he replied, at number seventeen Ursus argued:

> If I am not mistaken, not only my own hypotheses but also the Apollonian or pseudo-Tychonian hypotheses, which had been known to me

> for a long time from Copernicus, were imparted by me to Rollenhagen, the director of the school in Magdeburg. For in the year 1586, when I was on my way to Kassel, I visited Rollenhagen. I was welcomed and treated quite kindly by him, and when I left he voluntarily gave me traveling expenses. But he certainly harmed me in perhaps thinking that I was a runaway employee of Tycho, whose employee I never was nor wanted to be. Let Tycho therefore say who that runaway employee was, or how he could have escaped from him and that tiny island [Hven].[2]

As a general rule, Ursus defiantly emphasized his intellectual independence of Brahe. Yet at number twenty, where he was accused of theft, Ursus admitted:

> Let it be a theft, but it was intellectual. Learn to safeguard your possessions hereafter.[3]

XVII

KEPLER'S EVALUATION OF URSUS AS A MATHEMATICIAN AND ASTRONOMER

XVII

KEPLER'S EVALUATION OF URSUS AS A MATHEMATICIAN AND ASTRONOMER

Having dealt, first, with Ursus's abuse of his letter, and secondly, with Ursus's admitted intellectual theft, Kepler's letter to Herwart of 20/30 May 1599 then asked:

> In the third place, would you perhaps inquire whether Ursus's little book contains anything useful or excellent? For I do not know what you are most interested in. This is my answer. In astronomical matters, when it comes to understanding Ptolemy and Copernicus as system-builders, Ursus seems to have no knowledge (unless somebody would say that he is exceptionally bad). Nevertheless, nothing stops Ursus from being good in geometry, good in arithmetic. I myself am very eager to master the problems presented by him. Others also may be able to describe observational methods. But if he treated those problems, I would acknowledge that he is an astronomer, and I would not reject this little book. I cannot discuss the mysteries of sines and angles at present.[1]

As Ursus indicated on the title page of his *Astronomical Hypotheses*, in that book he discussed the "Construction of a Table of Sines, Minute by Minute, Exclusively by Means of Proportion" (sig. H4v-I2r); the "Solution of Triangles" (sig. I2v-3r); and the "Solution of All Triangles by the Method of Prosthaphaeresis, and Exclusively by Means of Sines" (sig. I3r-4r). Ursus also listed "Problems of the Process of Astronomical Observation" (sig. I4r-Klr). But he did not present the solutions to these problems because he did not wish to go to the expense of printing and illustrating them. In order to deal with Ursus's treatment of sines and angles, Kepler told Herwart:

> I would need Ursus's *Foundation of Astronomy*. The owner of a copy (which I got to know in town) is away on a trip. For in geometrical matters knowledge is certain, as you are aware, and either we know, or we know that we do not know, some axiom. In astronomy, on the other hand, there is room for opinions, as far as hypotheses are concerned. In geometry, therefore, nobody's discoveries are rejected; in astronomy certain persons must be ejected. As a result, whoever relies on the reasoning of anybody whom he has tested in geometry readily rejects and ignores all astronomers, as Ursus apparently does. For this, I suppose, in his thesis: "I understand geometry, I am lucky in finding new problems. Why would I not see the truth in astronomy too ahead of the others? Therefore, since astronomers refute one another, with confidence in my own thinking I shall disregard them all. For they are hard to understand, and time is needed to read them with discernment. I shall therefore save time, and spend it on more useful [occupations]." As the outcome of this attitude, accordingly, it is possible for Ursus to be uninformed about

the astronomy of the system-builders, yet ingenious and skillful in geometry. But Ursus wants an astronomer to be judged on the basis of his knowledge of geometry and arithmetic. It is of course true that anyone who lacks wings never raises himself aloft. But, on the other hand, it is not true that anyone having those Platonic wings [of arithmetic and geometry] for that reason knows at once how to fly too.[2]

XVIII

URSUS'S KNOWLEDGE OF CONTEMPORARY MATHEMATICIANS

XVIII

URSUS'S KNOWLEDGE OF CONTEMPORARY MATHEMATICIANS

Having evaluated Ursus's abilities as a mathematician and innovative astronomer, Kepler's letter to Herwart of 20/30 May 1599 proceeded to discuss contemporary mathematicians known to Ursus:

> In the next place, Ursus mentions certain
> 64 authors of whom he knows, like Viète, □
> Birckerus, Rubeus, and others, and whom he ranks with the outstanding mathematicians. None of them is known to me in this corner of Germany, in this isolation.[1]

At sig. H2v Ursus referred to an opponent whom he called the "greatest mathematician of this century after Viète." Little did Kepler realize that the writings of François Viète (1540-1603)

> were rare because he had them printed at his own expense and kept the copies in his own hands. As a man far removed from all desire for profit, he generously gave copies to his friends and to experts in these matters.[2]

Unfortunately for Kepler, he was neither a friend of Viète nor was he recognized as an expert in these matters when he wrote this letter to Herwart on 20/30 May 1599. After Viète, Kepler listed "Birckerus," intending to refer to "Johannes Georgius Brengkerus, a man who ... excels, surpasses, and outstrips Tycho in the science of mathematics," according to Ursus, whose quotation from Brengkerus mentions Byrgi.[3] Kepler somehow crossed Brengkerus with Byrgi to emerge with "Birckerus." The only work ever published by Jost Bürgi did not appear until 1620.[4] The only work ever published by Johann Georg Brengger

64. François Viète (1540-1603), the founder of modern algebra, was appointed on 25 March 1580 to the Maîtres des Requêtes, a chamber of royal counsellors authorized to hear requests for justice; from the portrait in their collection, this engraving was made by Nicolas-Henri Jacob (1782-1841)

did not appear until 1612;[5] in any case he was better known as a physician than as a mathematician. Incidentally, in publishing Kepler's letter at sig. Dlr-v, Ursus's *Astronomical Hypotheses* misprinted the writer's name as "Replerus," which was corrected by Ursus in his *Erratula* (sig. k1r)..

The last outstanding mathematician cited by Kepler from Ursus is Theodosius Rubeus (or Rossi, to give him his Italian surname). A "doctor of theology as well as of civil and canon law,"[6] he acquired the title of papal shieldbearer. With a special interest in the ecclesiastical calendar, he cultivated mathematics as a hobby. On 1 January 1593, from Rome he sent Ursus a query about the method of angle-division expounded, somewhat obscurely, in the Imperial Mathematician's *Foundation of Astronomy*, which Rubeus praised as "most ingenious" after having read and reread it. Rubeus sent the query at the request of his associate, Christopher Clavius (1537-1612), then the foremost scientist in the Jesuit order. In Rome they expected to finish printing Clavius's *Astrolabe* within two months, and Rubeus promised to send Ursus a copy. The Italian's courteous and respectful attitude toward Ursus explains why the latter printed Rubeus's letter on sig. F2v-3r of his *Astronomical Hypotheses.* Ursus seized the opportunity to contrast Rubeus's civility toward himself with Brahe's savage scorn. As for Kepler, he told Herwart:

> If I hear from Your Excellency which works by the authors named by Ursus are available, I shall instantly take care to obtain them for my use.[7]

In his reply of 20 July 1599, Herwart sent Kepler a copy of Clavius's *Astrolabe* (Rome, 1593) as well as of a work on recent northern voyages. Then he added:

> "Prenckerus" has published nothing.[8] I do not know Rubeus. François Viète..., outstanding in geometry and algebra, has published many

65. The marketplace in Munich, the capital of Bavaria

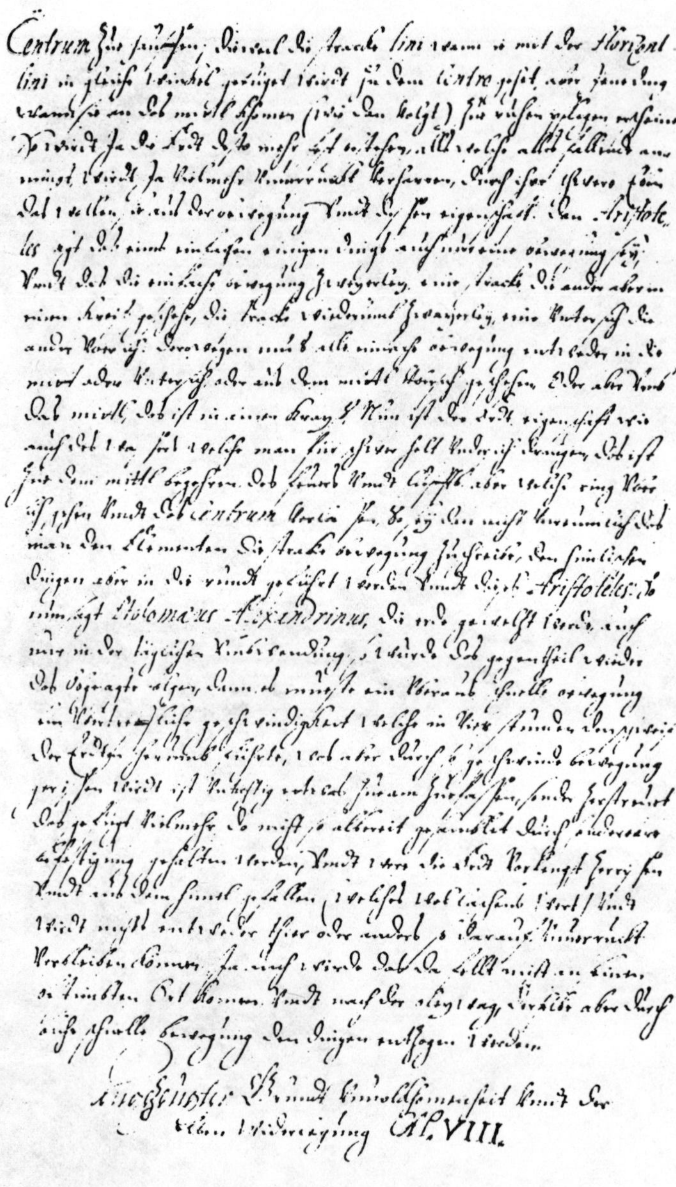

66. Folio 7 verso of Nicholas Reimers Ursus's translation of Copernicus's *Revolutions* from Latin into German , the earliest translation into any modern language

> works, most of which I myself am looking for,
> and I have not yet been able to acquire.[9]

Thus, with regard to Ursus's three oustanding mathematicians, Kepler "in this corner of Germany, in this isolation," did not fare much worse than Herwart, the wealthy chancellor of the duchy of Bavaria in its metropolitan capital, Munich.☐ Later on, Kepler obtained 65
access to the introduction which Bürgi wrote for his sine tables. Kepler recopied Bürgi's introduction with his own hand, and also edited it to some extent. He inserted material in Latin, which Bürgi never learned.[10] Because he could not read Copernicus's *Revolutions* in the original, Ursus translated it into German for him, thereby producing the first German translation of Copernicus's *Revolutions*.[11]☐ 66

XIX

KEPLER'S PREFERENCE FOR COPERNICUS OVER BRAHE

XIX

KEPLER'S PREFERENCE FOR COPERNICUS OVER BRAHE

After concluding that Ursus's hypotheses were derivative and not original, Kepler's letter to Herwart of 20/30 May 1599 proceeded to discuss the origin of Brahe's hypotheses:

> Finally, to say something also about Tycho's hypotheses, it is my judgment that he originated and discovered them. In addition, it is quite possible that he found them by himself without being guided by the Copernican theory.[1]

The recent misconception that Brahe derived his cosmic ideas from Reinhold's commentary on Copernicus's *Revolutions* was examined above.[2]

> The universe constructed by Brahe can easily be derived, however, from a modification of the Copernican theory.... Tycho has this unique advantage: he is free from that immense structure, the sphere of the fixed stars.[3]

Copernicus still believed in the old idea that all the stars were fixed in an otherwise invisible sphere. He pushed that sphere's bounding surface so far out into space, however, that his universe became almost infinite.[4] These gigantic dimensions of Copernicus's universe helped his successors to discard the obsolete concept of the sphere of the fixed stars. Apart from this difference, Kepler was confident that

> Everything else which Tycho will adduce from his very precise observations can easily be transferred to Copernicus, now and in the future. Take these two examples. The first is the variation in the distance of the fixed stars from the zodiac. Tycho asserts that he will demonstrate this by a shift in the latitudes of the fixed stars. But who does not prefer to say, with Copernicus, that the reason is the annual motion of the earth? It does not follow exactly the same path with respect to the stars every year. This is preferable to saying, with Tycho, that the whole sphere of the fixed stars tends toward the zodiac, that is, the earth's annual path. For, as you know [Kepler reminded Herwart], the zodiac, or the ecliptic, which is the line through its middle, is described in an annual motion, according to Ptolemy, by the sun, and by the earth, according to Copernicus.[5]

For his second example of how individual pieces of Brahe's cosmology could be accommodated in the Copernican, Kepler turned to a variation in the annual revolution:

> Tycho writes to me that the sun's orb expands.

For in his letter of 1/11 April 1598 to Kepler, Brahe had stated:

> The annual revolution ... does not seem to be always of the same size.[6]

But, as Kepler assured Herwart,

> Tycho's hypothesis is very highly refined, and quite credible to me. But I can say in a similar way that the earth's annual orbit expands, and the same effects will follow. For if either of the two orbs expands, the earth becomes

> nearer to Mars when that planet is in opposition to the sun [with the earth between Mars and the sun]; the earth becomes farther away from Mars when that planet is in conjunction with the sun [which is between Mars and the earth]. If the orb contracts, on the other hand, when Mars is in opposition to the sun the earth becomes farther away from Mars, and nearer to it when there is a conjunction of Mars and the sun.[7]

Having shown how a variation in the size of the annual orbit could fit into the Copernican system, Kepler then contended that such a variation, as a physical fact, would make more sense in Copernicus's universe than in Brahe's:

> In physical or cosmological discussions, however, the approach of the single earth to all five planets as its orb expands will be far more probable than the assertion that the spheres of the five planets, with the sun at their center, have risen away from the earth in an expanded circular framework.[8]

XX

KEPLER'S REPORT TO MAESTLIN ABOUT URSUS'S "ASTRONOMICAL HYPOTHESES"

XX

KEPLER'S REPORT TO MAESTLIN ABOUT URSUS'S "ASTRONOMICAL HYPOTHESES"

Kepler received a copy of Ursus's *Astronomical Hypotheses* on 15/25 May 1599 from Herwart, to whom he sent his opinion of that work on 20/30 May. On 10/20 July, Herwart informed Kepler that

> Tycho Brahe has already arrived in Prague, it is said, but he has not yet been granted an audience by the emperor, so that it is still not known whether he will settle down there or not.[1]

On 28 July/6 August 1599 Kepler informed Herwart:

> I have recommended Tycho's [*Astronomical*] *Letters* to our bookseller, but no books are brought to us [in Graz], this volume being blocked also on account of this investigation into heretical books.[2]

Then, in writing to Maestlin on 19/29 August 1599 Kepler said:

> I also lack Tycho's little book of [*Astronomical*] *Letters*. If there is a copy of it at Tübingen, I earnestly ask you to send it to me by the courier.[3]

In the same letter, Kepler reported to Maestlin

> about Ursus and Tycho. The noble Herwart, chancellor of the Bavarian court, a great expert in every branch of learning, sent me a copy of the little book by [Ursus], that flogger of Tycho. In it I finally saw my letter, which he inserted according to the following plan: with his discoveries and speculations he proposed to incite Tycho and Roeslin against himself.[4]

After making an objection to Roeslin, Ursus spoke about testing the accuracy of Kepler's view, "a summary of which ... he wrote to me in this letter that deserves to be printed."[5] But, as Kepler pointed out to Maestlin,

> Since Ursus mentions my little work registered at the Frankfurt fair, I do not know why he thinks this letter worth printing, except that it praises him. Whether he deleted anything from it, I do not know. What he prints is all mine. However, since I wrote [to him] several times, I am thoroughly convinced and I regard it as almost certain that from the very start I mentioned Tycho.[6]

Kepler's "almost certain" indicates a gnawing doubt that he mentioned Brahe in his first letter to Ursus. But he had no doubt whatever in reporting to Maestlin about the origin of Ursus's hypotheses:

> Ursus gives himself away like a squealing mouse, and in my judgment he is caught in the act by his own confession. According to his own declaration, he took his hypotheses from Ptolemy. For he did make some changes in Apollonius of Perga's proposition expounding the theory of the [planets'] stationary points.[7] But [according to Ursus] Tycho obtained his hypotheses from the same source,

and denies it.[8] Read what Ptolemy wrote about this subject, and you will say that Ursus is raving. It is of course true, since two propositions of Apollonius are cited by Ptolemy, that the later one to some extent does point the way to Tycho's hypotheses. For each of the three outer planets (since, as Ptolemy puts it neatly,[9] Apollonius's second proposition concerns only those [planets] that have every elongation [from the sun]) has its own eccentric, which completes an annual motion eastward. In addition, on each eccentric an epicycle turns while going around the earth. The epicycle's motion is westward, and equal [in angular displacement] to the planet's synodic motion [between successive oppositions]. Yet that utterly stupid man adduces, not this later proposition [of Apollonius], but the earlier one, which has absolutely nothing in common with Tycho. To support his contention, Ursus cites Copernicus, V, 35. In that chapter, Ursus argues without reservation, Copernicus guided Tycho to his hypotheses since, according to Ursus's explicit statement, the Tychonic hypotheses are present in Copernicus.[10] However, Copernicus recalls a theorem[11] relevant to Apollonius's earlier proposition. On the other hand, nothing is more ridiculous than Ursus's effort to drag these hypotheses of Tycho out of Copernicus, III, 25.[12] There Copernicus is talking about the center of the universe. Is the earth carried in an eccentric motion around the sun? Or is the sun borne in a very slow motion around the center of the Grand Orb, with the earth moving concentrically in an annual motion around the same center of the Grand Orb? Yet that jackass, who is no longer a bear, supposes that Copernicus is talking about transferring the sun to the circumference of the Grand Orb, with the earth in the center of that Orb. When I read that, I came to the conclusion that Ursus had neither read Ptolemy nor understood Copernicus.[13]

XXI

BRAHE'S REPORT TO KEPLER ABOUT URSUS

XXI

BRAHE'S REPORT TO KEPLER ABOUT URSUS

On 29 August 1599 Herwart informed Kepler that

> Tycho Brahe is touring the emperor's castles in Bohemia, looking for a suitable place to establish his residence and be free to attend to his celestial observations at an annual salary of 3000 florins (provided the rumor is correct), since he has been accepted by the emperor in his retinue. I would hope for such an appointment for you, and who knows what the Fates have in store?[1]

What the Fates had in store for Kepler was his appointment as Imperial Mathematician two days after the death of the Imperial Mathematician, Tycho Brahe. But in the meantime Kepler could not obtain a
67 copy of Brahe's *Astronomical Letters*□ in Graz because of the investigation into heretical books. Hence he welcomed Herwart's statement in this same letter of 29 August 1599:

> I am sending Tycho's *Astronomical Letters*, tied together with this letter. I would like Tycho's book returned, since I have no other copy.[2]

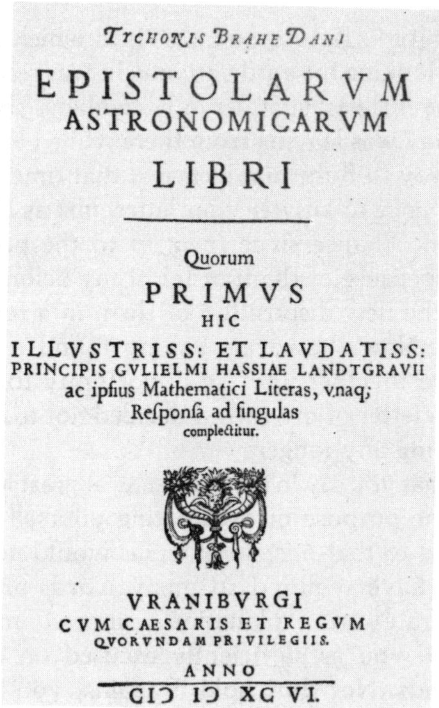

TYCHONIS BRAHE DANI

EPISTOLARVM
ASTRONOMICARVM
LIBRI

Quorum
PRIMVS
HIC
ILLVSTRISS: ET LAVDATISS:
PRINCIPIS GVLIELMI HASSIAE LANDTGRAVII
ac ipſius Mathematici Literas, v.naq;
Reſponſa ad ſingulas
complectitur.

VRANIBVRGI
CVM CAESARIS ET REGVM
QVORVNDAM PRIVILEGIIS.
ANNO
CIↃ IↃ XC VI.

67. Title Page of Tycho Brahe's *Astronomical Letters*, Uraniburg, 1596

But on 14 September 1599 Kepler regretfully told Herwart:

> You write that you are sending a copy of Tycho's [*Astronomical*] *Letters*. However, instead of that book, when I opened the wrapper, I receive[3]

other books. But Brahe himself sent Kepler a copy of his *Astronomical Letters*, as he told Kepler in a letter dated 9 December 1599,[4] and accepting Kepler's account of his involvement with Brahe's enemy:

> Even though I have not yet met you face to face, most learned sir, nevertheless I love you very dearly on account of the excellent qualities of your mind. Your extremely scholarly

> letter [of 9/19 February 1599], to which I had been looking forward very much, was received by me this past summer in Wittenberg, shortly before I was leaving from there while I was on my way to Bohemia. Hence at that time I had no chance to answer your letter, just as I have had no chance since then up to the present time because of the transfer of my belongings and the new disposition of them in a foreign land. Now, however, having found a little leisure together with an opportunity to send you a letter of my own, I decided not to delay replying any longer.
>
> What you say in the beginning at great length for the purpose of exculpating yourself with regard to that misplaced Ursus would not indeed have required so many words and so elaborate an explanation, since I myself regard you as sufficiently excused on other grounds. Nor do I hold it against you at all that he inserted your letter without your knowledge or consent in that defamatory and foul-mouthed writing which he published. As I now learn from you, he chopped up your letter and distorted it for the purpose of making himself look good, for this is perhaps what he had to do.[5]

Brahe suspected that Kepler's letter had been tampered with by Ursus when he published it in his *Astronomical Hypotheses* because in his letter to Brahe of 9/19 February 1599 Kepler doubted
(1) whether Ursus published Kepler's entire letter;
(2) whether Kepler said that "Ursus is thought much of by all scholars;" and
(3) how Kepler referred to Tycho, although he knew he did so.
Kepler's certainty (*fecisse tamen scio*) is certainly wrong.[6] But since Kepler's letter is known only from what Ursus published in his *Astronomical Hypotheses*,

it is impossible to decide whether Ursus altered it in any way. What stirred Brahe's wrath most of all was Ursus's (alleged) deletion of Kepler's honorific references to himself. Yet those references were not present in the letter, even before Ursus published it. Brahe's indignation in this regard, therefore, resulted from Kepler's faulty memory rather than from any misdeed by Ursus. Brahe's letter of 9 December 1599 to Kepler continued:

> The issue concerning his misappropriation of my hypotheses and publicizing them as his own would not be so grave had he not with most outrageous and criminal lies shamelessly attacked with his scurrilous and misshapen pen in that disreputable book teeming with falsehoods and insults my dignity and reputation, nay, my country, ancestry, and most honorable house, and defamed them as much as he can, and diffused such stuff in print to the public. On the other hand, he himself admits in his dedication that I deserve well of him.[7]

Amid the torrent of abuse aimed at Brahe by Ursus in his dedication, for rhetorical reasons he mixed a few kind words about "Tycho ... the very great astronomer, most industrious in observing, who deserves the very best from me."[8] Brahe's onslaught against Ursus continued in his letter of 9 December 1599 to Kepler:

> In addition, I have a certain poem of his. Even though it babbles along in his (customary) manner, it is written with his own hand and thanks me not only for plying him liberally with food and drink during several days while he was with me once in Uraniburg, but also for giving him money when he was leaving. Look at how he thanks me for these and other [favors]![9]

Ursus's poem, found among the manuscripts in St. Petersburg (now Leningrad), was addressed to "Tycho Brahe, the very great astronomer." It began by reminding Brahe that for a week he wined and dined Ursus, to whom he also gave money, while Ursus was penniless. He wrote this poem with his own hand, and signed it your "dear friend."[10] In his letter of 9 December 1599, Brahe proceeded to tell Kepler what infuriated Ursus in the first place:

> As the springboard for these criminal actions, Ursus utilized the presence in my *Astronomical Letters,* volume I, of a letter written by the Landgrave's mathematician, Christopher Rothmann, in which he calls Ursus a dirty scoundrel.[11]

Brahe labeled his *Astronomical Letters* volume I in the expectation that he would be able to publish additional volumes, which never materialized. Many of the letters in this first volume were exchanged with the Landgrave of Hesse William IV and his mathematician Christopher Rothmann. Complying with the Landgrave's instructions, Rothmann sent his first letter to Brahe from Kassel, the Landgrave's residence, on 14 April 1586.[12] In this letter Rothmann did not mention Ursus. Nor did he do so in his second letter, dated 26 August 1586.[13] Nevertheless, when Rothmann's second letter was printed in Brahe's *Astronomical Letters,* it condemned Ursus as "that dirty scoundrel" (*impuro illo nebulone*).[14]

How did this contemptuous expression get into Rothmann's letter of 26 August 1586, as published in Brahe's *Astronomical Letters*? This volume was dedicated by Brahe on 21 March 1596, four years after the death of Landgrave William, to his son and successor, Landgrave Maurice (1572-1632). In the dedication Brahe pointed out that copies of Landgrave William's letters

> were undoubtedly still preserved in your chancellor's archives, so that anybody will readily infer that I have interpolated nothing in them of my own (an action which otherwise would in itself have been a crime.)[15]

The handwritten drafts of Landgrave William's letters retained in Kassel could easily be compared with the printed versions to see whether there were any discrepancies. In like manner the printed versions of Rothmann's letters could readily have been compared with the manuscript drafts on file in Kassel. But the condemnation of Ursus in the printed version of Rothmann's letter of 26 August 1586, although not present in the handwritten draft of that letter, provoked no comment at that time.[16] What is more, in his letter to Rothmann of 21 February 1589 Brahe referred to Ursus

> on whom, in a certain letter sent to me, you once pinned a worthy label, calling him a dirty scoundrel.[17]

In his reply on 22 August 1589 Rothmann, without protesting that he had not used this expression, remarked:

> I would also write about that Ursus of Dithmarschen and his theft of your system of the world, but the courier is in a hurry, so that I shall postpone that subject for another time.[18]

With the courier waiting impatiently for him, Rothmann had to omit a lengthy section which is preserved in the manuscript draft in Kassel. In that omitted section Rothmann planned to tell Brahe, among other things, that in Kassel Ursus

> bragged that he had worked as a typesetter in your printing shop,

and Rothmann concluded: "I don't want ... to have

anything to do with that dirty"[19] man. Although Brahe did not see the omitted section, he heard the full story of Ursus's stay in Kassel from the lips of Rothmann, who visited Hven during the month of August 1590.[20] Hence, when Rothmann's letter of 26 August 1586, which did not mention Ursus, was published by Brahe, he felt no compunction in retrojecting into it Rothmann's later, savagely hostile, attitude toward Ursus. In this instance, what Brahe had called a crime in his dedication of the *Astronomical Letters*, namely, editorial interpolation of material not present in the handwritten letter as received by him, he condoned as a justifiable modification. Thus, in the omitted section of the letter of 22 August 1589 Rothmann called Ursus "dirty" (*impuro*). In his conversations with Brahe in August 1590 Rothmann may have added "scoundrel" (*nebulone*). In the letter of 26 August 1586, as printed, Brahe has Rothmann call Ursus "that dirty scoundrel." No wonder Brahe suspected Ursus of manipulating Kepler's letter when he published it in his *Astronomical Hypotheses*.

Having called Ursus a "dirty scoundrel," Brahe's letter to Kepler of 9 December 1599 continued:

> For that is what he was in the Landgrave's court. Rothmann learned this not only from experience but also from the reports of others in those places where Ursus had lived previously. In another letter to Rothmann, however, I repeat this expression merely by quoting it.[21] At the same time I hint at the scheme by which he surreptitiously removed certain of my papers, some of which I recovered. These are written with his own hand (which he cannot deny). I still have them in my possession. Had more serious occupations left me the leisure, at the time when those letters were being printed on my press, to review them at least with regard to their individual contents, I would surely not have permitted

> that book [*Astronomical Letters*] published by me to be besmirched by the name of that beastly and stinking Ursus. The reason is not that he can be deemed undeserving of the application of such an appellation or that he would suffer any harm from language agreeing with the customary judgment of mankind. Not only Rothmann has this view of him, but also many others who have known him enough. The true reason is that in my writings I do not deliberately assail anybody's life and character, whatever they may be. Hence, also in the letter of His Excellency Jacob Kurtz, of blessed memory, which I later appended at Wandsbek to my book on *Astronomical Instruments*,[22] I omitted Ursus's name, although Jacob Kurtz denounced him eloquently and in addition labeled him my plagiarist.[23]

In his letter of 28 June 1590, Kurtz did label Ursus a plagiarist of Brahe. But in keeping with his usual practice, in his *Astronomical Instruments* Brahe replaced Ursus's name by the abbreviation *N.N.* (*Nomen Nescio*),[24] thereby pretending not to know the name of the individual being denounced. Yet in the previous year Ursus's *Astronomical Hypotheses* had already quoted Kurtz's denunciation of Ursus as a plagiarist.[25] For, as the Imperial Vice-Chancellor, Kurtz could readily circulate copies of his letter to Brahe, denouncing Ursus, the Imperial Mathematician-designate, as a plagiarist of Brahe. One such copy is preserved in the Bodleian Library.[26]

Ursus, however, fought back by trying to pull the teeth out of Kurtz's bite. For, Ursus argued that Kurtz was

> talking in Tycho's manner and in agreement with a common mistake, either ironically and jokingly, or perhaps because he thought the situation was as Tycho had described it to him

> and had complained to him, namely, that I actually swiped my hypotheses from Tycho. For, most vigorously and indeed overzealously before my arrival at the Imperial Court, Kurtz attributed these hypotheses to Tycho, regarding him in the popular way as absolutely flawless or incapable of error. Afterwards, however, in the year 1591, on the basis of Tycho's little book on *The New Star of 1572*, I manifestly proved to Kurtz and convinced him that there were six defects in Tycho. The fourth was that the hypotheses which he falsely claims for himself, and which he boasts are his own, publicizes, and displays (in another book [*Stella caudata*]), are explicitly set forth in Copernicus.[27]

Brahe continued his letter of 9 December 1599 to Kepler by explaining why Ursus's name appeared in print in his *Astronomical Letters*:

> It happened, however, that this task of proofreading the printed sheets in that volume of the [*Astronomical*] *Letters* was entrusted by me to certain students of mine. I gave them the originals just as they were written by hand. They thought that nothing was to be changed, and did not venture to ask me any questions while I was occupied with other, more important matters. Hence they allowed everything to be printed just as they had it in manuscript. Thus, through a certain inadvertency it came about that Ursus's name together with the associated epithets was retained there.[28]

Kurtz's letter was printed in Brahe's *Astronomical Instruments* of 1598, and Rothmann's in Brahe's *Astronomical Letters* of 1596. Brahe followed the same system of printing and proofreading in both of these volumes. Ursus's name was removed from the *Astro-*

nomical Instruments, after it had been printed in the *Astronomical Letters*. In his letter to Kepler of 9 December 1599, Brahe went on to question whether his *Astronomical Letters'* derogatory mention of Ursus warranted the vehemence of the latter's reaction in his *Astronomical Hypotheses*:

> But we shall soon see whether this is a sufficient and sufficiently just reason for heaping contempt on me and my family, and to that extent on my country, with such exceedingly unbalanced malice. Ursus could readily have complained about the damage, if any were inflicted on him, and remedied it by legitimate means, and not raged with such an ineffectual feeling out of a desire for unbridled revenge, and made everything far worse. Yet there is no reason why you should think that I am more highly aroused against that trifler than my situation permits, as you say (with sincere feeling, to be sure), since I do not deem the matter to deserve the emperor's displeasure (as a certain individual[29] advised me in writing). But since Ursus deliberately tried to degrade me in violation of law and justice and in opposition to the most praiseworthy imperial statutes by means of a more than infamous publication contrary to all truth and my record, I shall see to it that he is taken to court and convicted and punished according to law. He fled into Silesia from Prague shortly after my arrival there. But, as I found out, he recently returned secretly, perhaps because he had learned that I was no longer there. Yet he will feel how long my hands are, even if I am not present in person, when he will soon be arrested and afterwards summoned to judgment.
>
> But since I learn from your letter that you have not seen those filthy and scurrilous

> pages, I am sending you a copy so that you may have a more convenient view of your letter there and judge what the rest is like. In any case you will see how crazy, foul-mouthed, criminal, and putrid a compilation it is and how thoroughly it gives off its author's odor. Perhaps you have never seen more outrageous insults, abhorrent to the ears of all upright and honest persons. But [this is] more than enough about that wild Dithmarschen Bear, since he does not deserve such a stream of words from you or me. If you knew him from the inside and (as they say) under the skin (I am not now talking about the French disease, of which he has plenty on account of his immoral life), you would testify as I do, indeed, you would have so testified long ago.
>
> I shall add only one thing, for the sake of claiming my hypotheses, although it is a very small matter and I have many more and stronger arguments on hand. Ursus is not afraid to ascribe to himself those hypotheses which I first devised in the year 1584. Will anybody believe that he really originated them who knows that he never was familiar with any celestial observations from which new hypotheses arise? Indeed, if he cannot demonstrate in all its details the apparent place of a single planet, especially one of the three outer planets, by this recent theory (as he scarcely can), what intelligent person, I ask, will he convince that the innovation is his?[30]

In this letter to Kepler, Brahe dealt with a number of other astronomers whom he accused of claiming priority in devising his "new hypotheses," and he also raised several objections to Kepler's *Cosmographic Mystery*. Then Brahe continued:

But I shall discuss these and other topics with you at greater length with pleasure and much intensity, and I shall hand you more of my writings if you visit me some day, as you promise. This will now be less onerous to you than previously, since at the present time I have established my new astronomical abode in Bohemia, not very far away from you, and I live in the imperial castle in Benátky, 5 miles from Prague.[31] For I suppose that you have previously learned from others (since I have already been here half a year) that I was most graciously invited here from Germany by His Imperial Majesty and welcomed most cordially and generously. Yet I would not want hard luck to force you to come to me, but rather your own judgment as well as your love and affection for the studies which we share. Nevertheless, whatever comes to pass, you will find in me not a follower of fortune, whatever that may be, but your friend who even under untoward circumstances will not fail you with his advice and help, but rather will advance you to everything that is best. And if you arrive soon, perhaps we shall find arrangements which will hereafter be more advantageous for you and your family than previously.

Farewell. When you answer, send your letter to Dr. Blotius of Vienna, who is in charge of the Imperial Library there. He will readily forward it to Prague, whence it will reach me promptly. Again, most auspicious farewell. I wrote in Benátky or the Venice of the Bohemians on 9 December in the new style, 1599.

Your most affectionate
Tycho Brahe
I wrote with my own hand.[32]

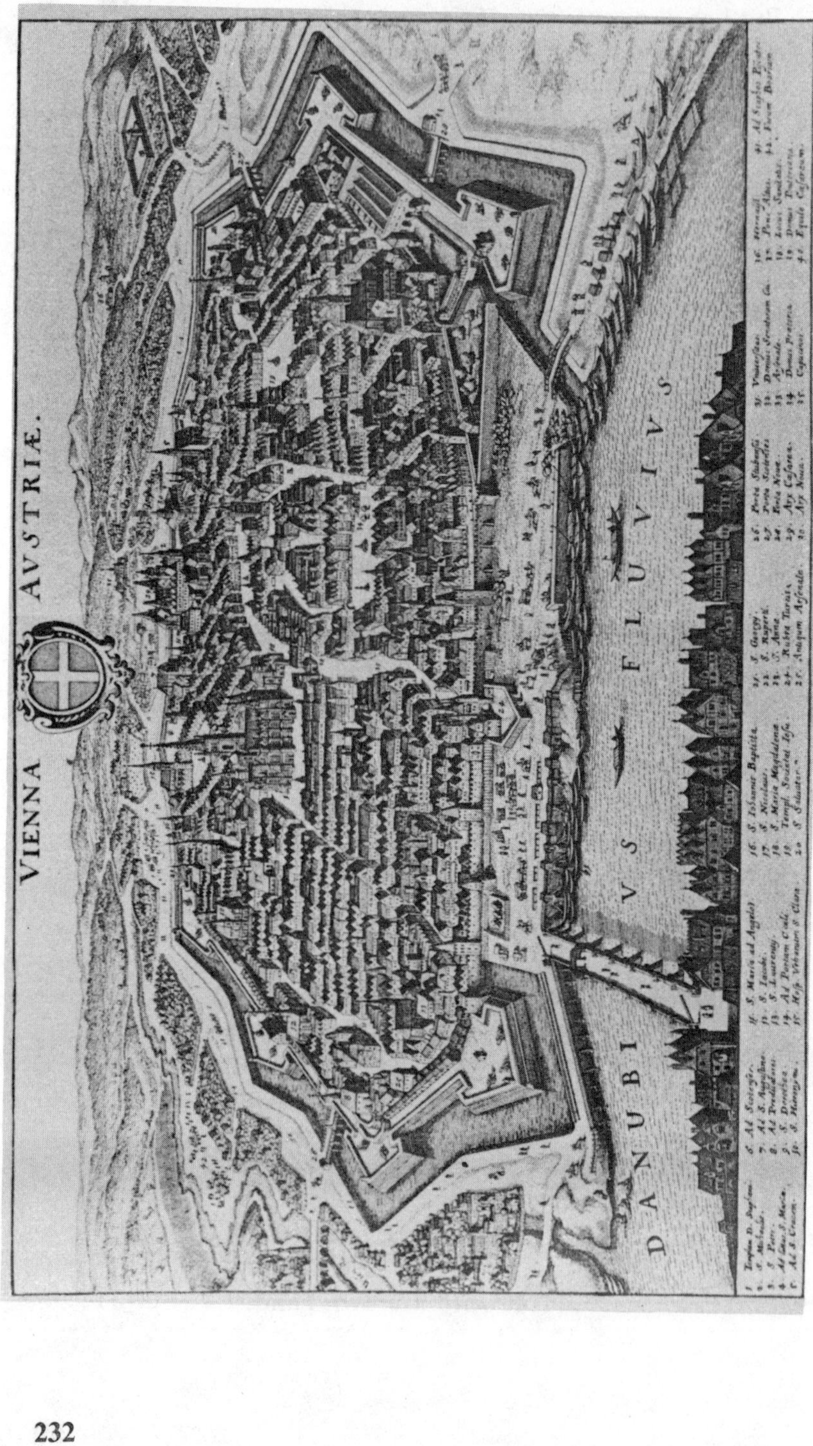

68. Vienna, engraving by Matthaeus Merian Sr.

Five days after writing the foregoing letter to Kepler, on 14 December 1599 Brahe addressed the following request to Dr. Hugo Blotius (1533-1608) in Vienna: □ 68

> I ask you not to be annoyed by forwarding through a reliable intermediate courier the message attached to this letter, together with certain books, addressed to Johannes Kepler, the distinguished mathematician in Styria, whether he is there or anywhere else in that area. Previously he lived in the city of Graz. I do not know whether he is still there, since I have learned that their affairs are in disarray. If you receive any response from him, send it to Prague, to the aforementioned Dr. Heller. It will reach me promptly.[33]

Brahe dispatched his letter to Kepler five days after he had written it, because he had to leave Benátky in a hurry. So Kepler was informed by Herwart, writing from Munich on that same day, 14 December 1599:

> Up to now I have received no further letter from Tycho Brahe. The reason is that because the plague is raging he had to flee from that Venice of Bohemia, for that is how the place is called which the emperor assigned him as his residence.[34]

Brahe was back in Benátky by 26 January 1600, when he wrote to Kepler:

> The employees whom I had sent to Prague returned late last night, unexpectedly bringing, most distinguished and dearest Kepler, your very kind letter. When I read it, I learned with great joy that you are now in Prague. Yet I was disappointed to be informed by them that you have not yet received the letter which about a month ago, in prompt response to your most recent letter, I sent to Vienna so that, through Dr. Blotius, it would be for-

> warded to you, wherever you had gone. If it had been delivered to you in the meantime, you would have overlooked this repeated avowal and excuse in this matter, which does not deserve so many words, and you would have hurried here right away (since you are in the vicinity), dispensing with any further hesitation and delay. Again and again I ask you to still do so. You will be able to accompany in the same carriage the noble and learned youth, my employee, Franz Tengnagel, and my older son Tycho, whom I am now dispatching to Prague to attend to certain private business in my name there. For they will, God willing, return here in a few days, and they will easily find a place for you in the carriage.[35]

Dr. Blotius in Vienna did not forward Brahe's letter of 9 December 1599 to Kepler for the simple reason that he was not informed about Kepler's movements. After Kepler returned to Graz, he explained to Herwart on 12 July 1600:

> On 11 January [1600] I left Graz to visit Tycho. I stayed in Prague several days, and finally reached Benátky on 5 February. From that day until 1 June, if you omit about three weeks, I lived uninterruptedly with Tycho and in his household. He had invited me a second time (for you know about his first invitation) by means of an exceptionally kind letter. Yet I did not receive that letter until 10 June in Vienna on my way back [to Graz]. Thus my arrival [in Benátky] was not only welcome but also anticipated. At the present time it would take too long to report what I saw, what I learned. You yourself indicated to me the upshot of the report in very accurate language: there is no fear that I would regret

> the trip.[36] For he wanted to reimburse me for my travel expenses, and he advanced me the money necessary for my return trip as far as Vienna. The gist of our agreement was that Tycho would obtain for me a letter of the emperor by which I would be called to Bohemia for two years to supervise Tycho's publications, and yet I could hold on to my salary in Styria. He would supply the money needed to move my family. To these proposals presented by me, he added that he would see to it that I would receive at least a hundred thalers more in Bohemia.... Together with Tycho's letter, which I mentioned above, in Vienna I received his *Instruments* and *Astronomical Letters*.[37]

In addition to these two books by Tycho, in Vienna Kepler found the letter of 9 December 1599 in which Brahe poured forth his resentment and hatred of Ursus.

XXII

A WITNESS FOR BRAHE: RODOLPHE MEHERENC

XXII

A WITNESS FOR BRAHE: RODOLPHE MEHERENC

Kepler's letter of 9/19 February 1599 to Brahe did not reach him until the summer of that year, while he was on his way to Bohemia. Since the plague was raging there, he waited in Wittenberg for it to subside. But he had no opportunity to answer Kepler's letter in Wittenberg, and did not do so until 9 December 1599, when he was established in Benátky.

Living with him at this time was Rodolphe Méhérenc, a student from Sées in France, who had previously met Kepler in Graz. When the plague broke out in Benátky, both Brahe and Méhérenc took refuge in the imperial castle in Giertziga [Jiřice], three German miles (or twelve statute miles) northeast of Prague. On 14 December 1599 Brahe wrote his aforementioned letter to Dr. Blotius from Giertziga, and two days later, on Saturday, 16 December, Méhérenc wrote to Kepler as follows:

> Hearing from Tycho (with whom I am now staying) that a letter is being sent to you, I thought it would not be amiss if I took the opportunity to write something recalling our friendly and very cordial conversation in the school in Graz. The effect produced by pride, refinement, and jealousy, especially on those

who apparently control the population and affairs, has finally been experienced to the full by those whose acquaintance you shared with me. Not in vain, perhaps, did I sometimes offer the example of my country France, which I ought now to be witnessing if the fates had decreed what you intimated and forecast calmly, although not unintelligibly yet quite openly.[1]

Meanwhile, from your letter [of 9/19 February 1599] to Tycho I have learned that there are certain people, including that Ursus of Dithmarschen, who dare to claim for themselves the new hypotheses first devised by Tycho. Yet I can testify that I went to Denmark at the end of the year [15]87, and thereafter on 6 January [15]88 to the island of Hven with a recommendation to Tycho from His Excellency, Charles de Danzay, the French ambassador, of blessed memory.[2] In Hven, among Tycho's books, I found the one dealing with the comet of the year 1577.[3] [Before August of] the previous year, that is, 1587, it was completely printed and finished in Tycho's printing shop. Yet because he intended it to be distributed closer [to the published date], he wanted it to be cited as though it had been published in the year [15]88. In that book's Chapter VIII, this hypothesis which is in controversy is expounded by Tycho. Afterwards, in August of the same year [1588] in Strasbourg Ursus published [in his *Foundation of Astronomy*] a similar hypothesis as his own discovery which, however, had been printed in the said book [Brahe's *Stella caudata*] more than a whole year earlier.

Accordingly, who will be able in any way to attribute that discovery to himself and take it away from Tycho, who was the first to publish it but made no claim to it? I can testify that what I have said is true, since with my own eyes I saw that book about the comet printed on the island of Hven in the year [15]87, when nothing about this hypothesis had been previously printed by anybody. I believed that I should tell you about this so that you would be informed about the originator [of the hypothesis]. For Ursus evidently convinced many people otherwise, just as you too through lack of information do not hesitate to ascribe it to Ursus in the letter [of 15 November 1595] which he inserted in his infamous book [*On Astronomical Hypotheses*].

I ask you in my name to greet the highborn and noble lord, Hans Sigismund Wagn, if you have the opportunity. May Almighty God preserve you and him, together with all our other friends, in the best of health, security, and happy march of events. Farewell.[4]

XXIII

TWO OTHER WITNESSES FOR BRAHE: HANSEN AND WALTER

XXIII

TWO OTHER WITNESSES FOR BRAHE: HANSEN AND WALTER

Together with his letter of 29 November/9 December 1599 to Kepler, Brahe forwarded copies of two documents, as he noted in the postscript:

> Among my papers I found ... a copy of a letter from a certain Christen Hansen, a Dane,
> 69 who is now in Leiden□ as a student, and was part of my household when my book on the comet of the year [15]77 was being printed in Uraniburg. He arrived a little after Ursus had been with me, and therefore he found out from my other students how deceitfully Ursus had behaved.[1]

Writing in Latin, Brahe give Hansen's name as *Christianus* (or *Christiernus*) *Johannis*.[2] This surname, a patronymic in the genitive case, means John's (son) = Hansen. The nominative case, *Johannes*, is inappropriate as a surname.[3] Christianus or Christiernus was Hansen's given name, not his surname.[4] Since he came from Ribe in Jutland, he called himself *Ripensis*, but his surname was not Riber.[5] Born in 1567, he arrived in Hven on 27 April 1586.[6] He may have been accompanied by his father, who left on 10 November 1586.[7] Apart from two excursions to Copenhagen and

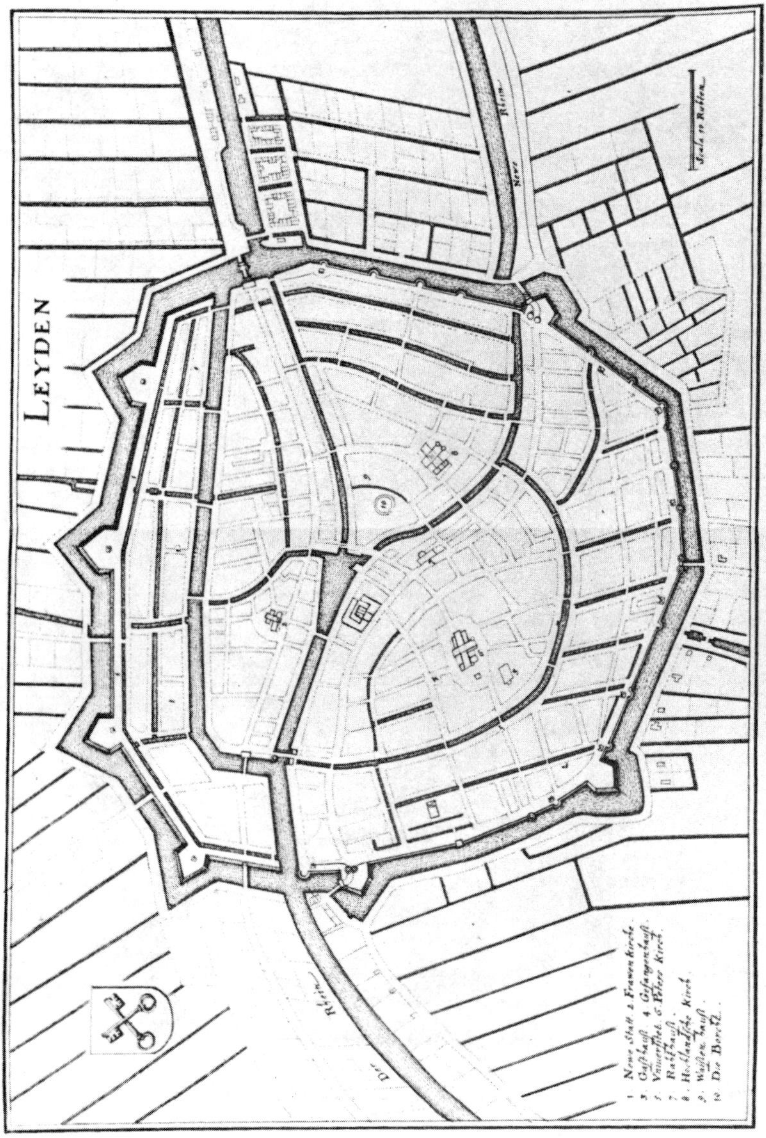

69. Leiden, where Joseph Justus Scaliger (1540-1609) taught at the local university

70. Joseph Justus Scaliger, aged 35

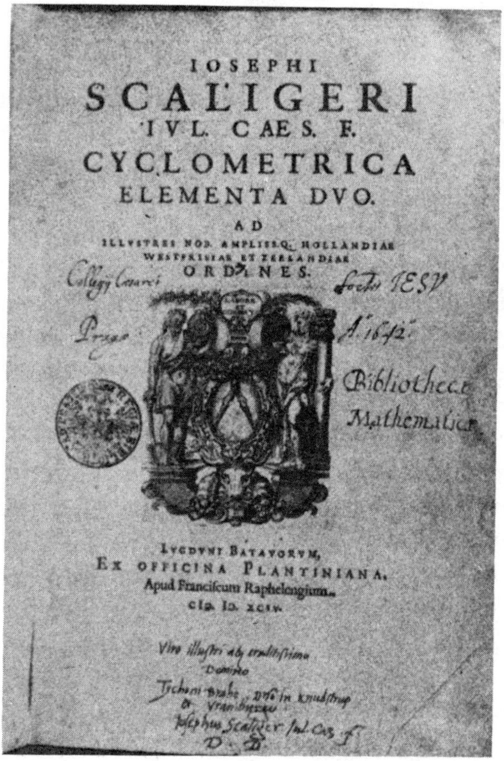
IOSEPHI
SCALIGERI
IVL. CAES. F.
CYCLOMETRICA
ELEMENTA DVO.
AD
ILLVSTRES NOB. AMPLISSQ. HOLLANDIAE WESTFRISIAE ET ZEELANDIAE ORDINES.
LVGDVNI BATAVORVM,
EX OFFICINA PLANTINIANA,
Apud Franciscum Raphelengium.
CIƆ. IƆ. XCIV.

71. Title Page of J.J. Scaliger's presentation copy of his *Cyclometrica* (Leiden, 1594) to Tycho Brahe

Lübeck,[8] he spent four years with Brahe, departing on the 24th[9] (not the 23rd)[10] of April 1590. After leaving Hven, Hansen sent his former mentor valuable astronomical observations. Thus, he reported on the lunar eclipse of 14 June 1592 from Wittenberg,[11] and on the solar eclipse of 20 May 1593 from Zerbst in Anhalt.[12] There, from 22 July to 24 August, he watched the comet of 1593, which Brahe in Uraniburg could not see.[13] After returning to Denmark in 1594,[14] Hansen sent Brahe his observation of the solar eclipse of 23 September 1595 from Strasbourg.[15] Back again in Jutland, he reported to Brahe his observation of the solar eclipse of 24 February 1598.[16] Not long thereafter he went to study with the renowned scholar

70, 71 Joseph Justus Scaliger□□ (1540-1609) in the University of Leiden.[17] There on 13 May 1598 he sent Brahe the letter of which a copy was transmitted to Kepler:

> To the noble and most excellent
> Tycho Brahe, my cherished sponsor:
>
> While I was on my way to Leiden, I recently happened to come across a work [*Astronomical Hypotheses*] by Reimers Ursus that was published in Prague last year. It is exceedingly vicious and worthless, being all full of the stupidest lies in addition to the abominable insults directed against you. It made me very unhappy and to the same degree boiling over with justified rage. I could not rest until I sent you some notice of it, being impelled thereto by the obligations of my situation linked with my very deep regard [for you]. For the present I shall say nothing, noble sir, about the insults directed against you (which I leave, with their author, to be repressed by appropriate punishment).
>
> How impudent, I ask you, is this Ursus, who does not shrink from shameless lies, from unscrupulous fabrications, as if he had been the first creator and originator of your hypothesis? It is a crime that what he could not even grasp or understand, he was not ashamed to call his own and invented by himself! Indeed, if he appeared before your Astronomy's trial chamber, where an explanation[18] of the relative sizes of the spheres in the hypothesis is being rendered, he would defend himself in vain by falsely pretending that he had already thought it out either in a corner of Poland or somewhere or other in Pomerania. Indeed, overpowered by his conscience, if there is any in the foul-mouthed man, that thief (since he does not wish to be labeled a plagiarist, even

though that is what Martial calls the one who stole his books)[19] of his own accord with his disgraceful ignorance would willy-nilly admit that he took this [hypothesis] from you and your observatory. This is the situation, most noble Tycho Brahe.

For in recent years he went to Uraniburg with the most noble lord Eric Lange, in whose service he was at that time. Among other things, he found out that you had told the most noble lord Lange about certain astronomical principles recently devised by you. Being inquisitive, without your knowledge he examined all the corners of the library, all your papers, until he chanced to come across a certain small sheet on which your hypothesis was sketched, incorrectly and doubtless casually by one of your students. Ursus swiped it. After he went to Germany, he displayed it far and wide not only to the most illustrious Landgrave of Hesse but also to other most distinguished men, as though it were his own, discovered by himself, showing it off not otherwise than a jackass carrying a sacrament. For had he even incidentally merely made obeisance to astronomy's sanctuary, at least he would have recognized the error and marked as mistaken this relative proportion of the spheres by which forsooth Mars's sphere encloses the sun's path but does not intersect it, as was required. These configurations once reduced Copernicus to an absurd position. So, I say, they drove Ursus, master of evil,[20] to an unrestrained passion for insults to take refuge[21] in all sorts of abuse and every madness directed against you.

By the same token it is absolutely certain that your book on the comet of the year [15]77 was printed on your own press in Uraniburg toward the end of the year [15]87. (Yet later you decided on the year [15]88 as the imprint, perhaps so that the book would be to this extent more recent and more salable if you wanted the copies to be distributed that quickly. I have heard from others that you delayed for definite reasons, for instance, that your remaining works might be finished in the meantime). As a result, after Ursus, who was then in Strasbourg, learned that this book of your had been issued, worrying that he might suffer the pain of having your big morsel snatched from his jaws, he quickly looked to his own advantage and made his move. In that same year [15]88, in the month of August, he arranged to have what he calls his *Foundation of Astronomy* published in Strasbourg, not knowing that your book (in about the middle of which your system[22] of spheres was contained) had been printed during the previous year in Uraniburg in your native land. I could absolutely affirm this as a living witness,[23] together with many others of us who were your astronomical research assistants. Hence, although Ursus tries to defend and protect his plagiarism, he toils in vain, recklessly and insolently advertising himself as its originator. I need not mention that you did not in the least derive the hypothesis from a statement by the Landgrave's mathematician, Christopher Rothmann (as is falsely feigned by Ursus).

Finally, there is the matter of Apollonius of Perga, from whom Ursus charges that you obtained this arrangement of the hypotheses. His purpose in this wicked endeavor is to convince others that at least the arrangement is not yours, if he could not establish it as his own, as if he might still cause damage to some extent. All of us who were your pupils and examined your whole library whenever we wanted to, without any hesitation testify that it contained no work by Apollonius dealing with hypotheses, nor did you have any other of his books except his treatise on *Conic Sections*, in which no such material is found.

As for Ursus's desire to intimate that Copernicus proposed something of this sort and hinted at this hypothesis, no rebuttal is required in my opinion. For it is quite clear to those who read and understand Copernicus's writings that these allegations were adduced in bad faith by this malicious man and do not smack of the true opinion of that very great man Copernicus. You could demonstrate this very well from Copernicus himself (if you deemed it worthwhile to answer this detractor, an action for which I know and recognize that you are too important). Let others perhaps do so, even if you judge him unworthy of a refutation, and deservedly so, for how would you cure Ursus's wild insanity?

It is certainly true that once, while he was still working in Denmark for Eric Lange, he was transported to such a degree of frenzy that, having burned most of his books, he was afraid of being pilloried. His giddy brain was so deranged that over and over again he threw himself as a suppliant at the feet of Lange, until the latter wanted nothing more than to get rid of him. How he behaved in Germany, especially in Kassel, Strasbourg, and other places, I shall not say here, since it is quite clear, and there is no need for me to make any statement.

Accordingly, most noble and most excellent sir, do not be affected by the contumacious insults of this fierce Ursus. On the contrary, like the moon on high ignoring the barking of a mad dog, disregard this damage done to your

> Excellency, being definitely convinced there will be no informed men, endowed with true virtue and learning, who will not read this exceedingly malicious and infamous book with the indignation it deserves, and who will pray for and prognosticate evil for this evil Ursus.
>
> Farewell, most cherished sponsor. I urgently ask you to forgive my copiousness in writing.
>
> Leiden, 13 May 1598, new style
>
> Your noble Excellency's
>
> most humble servant
> Christian Hansen of Ribe
> with his own hand[24]

What Hansen wrote about Ursus was based on hearsay. But eyewitness testimony was provided by Lange's secretary, Michael Walter. Doubtless in compliance with a request from Lange, acting on behalf of Brahe, on 23 May 1598 in Kassel before a notary public Walter drew up an affidavit. A copy of Walter's affidavit, accompanying a copy of Hansen's letter written ten days earlier, was transmitted to Kepler by Brahe together with his letter of 29 November/9 December 1599. The notary put the following heading on Walter's deposition:

> Affidavit of Erich Lange's Secretary concerning
> What He Knows about Ursus of Dithmarschen

The affidavit was written out by Walter with his own hand:

> List of Several Extracts of What I Know about a Person Named Nicholas Ursus of Dithmarschen, who worked for my lord, the noble and honorable Erich Lange
>
> When Ursus came to my lord, he looked as though his actions promised something proper and gifted. From day to day, however, he turned out quite different on account of his needless gossiping, and the mischievous arguments he got into with shepherds and other

good people, as well as the many other peculiarities he exhibited. Daily experience, moreover, then further disclosed that sometimes he lost his mind so that everybody took him for very much a visionary and a fool, and my lord himself was annoyed over it.

Later on my lord traveled from Jutland to Zeeland, and during the journey visited Tycho Brahe. He took this Ursus along, because he demanded it so insistently of my lord. My lord traveled to the island Hven, took him along, and stayed there for full 14 days with the noble Tycho Brahe. While these lords were entertaining each other with lively conversation, nobody noticed Ursus. Secretly he poked about the house among Tycho Brahe's instruments and other constructions, and made drawings of them. Since no students were in session, and Tycho Brahe's books and writings were available, he could surreptitiously get hold of them too, as he himself told me. My lord Tycho was warned by one of his students, and it was perhaps beneath his Excellency's dignity to be actively running all over the place.

Together with my lord, he informed another student by the name of Andreas[25] [of Viborg in Jutland], who sometimes for the fun of it let himself get involved in all sorts of arguments with Ursus. Brahe asked Andreas whether he had any advice in this matter. Andreas was confident he would find out what was going on, and therefore spent the night in Ursus's room. Quietly testing whether Ursus had any such stuff on him, in one side of his pants Andreas found four whole handfuls of tracings and writings. But when he wanted to look on the other side, he was afraid that because Ursus was stirring, he would become aware, and therefore Andreas could search no further. When Ursus woke up in the morning, he discovered that not all the surreptitiously written documents were there. Like a raving maniac, he ran around shrieking, weeping, and screaming so that he could hardly be calmed down. It pained him that he had been found out and his secret tricks uncovered, so that the lords and all of us saw his extreme madness, and had a good time over it. Both lords assured him that anything among the papers that belonged to him and did not concern Tycho Brahe would certainly be recovered by him. This also happened, as we all knew.

Then, when he left the area with my lord and we returned to Bygholm[26], day by day he slid further and further into delirium and madness. He imagined, and said openly, that my lord wanted to have him hanged; that is what the overseer would construct at the house; I too would do the same, and want to stab him, and people intended to end his life. When my lord received the royal marshal Peter Guldenstern, Ursus fell on his knees before him and begged him to plead that Ursus should not be hanged. He acted abominably, wept, and howled, and imagined all sorts of things that my lord or his servants never thought of, but wondered that he behaved so strangely. When he was quietly advised not to imagine such things and ask God for mercy, he declared and acknowledged he had forsaken God's word and teaching. At the same time he said he thought that at night something like a ghost came to his bed and wanted to drag him off. When he was in bed at night in his room, he also began to shout out loud and scream as if somebody wanted to haul him away. As a result my lord was inclined to send him to one of his estates, called Engelsholm, where Ursus would be all by himself, to see whether he could undergo a change. Yet he remained as mad as he was, so that from time to time he threw his own books into the stove and burned them up. My lord's mother, who was there at the time, had to lock the room where the books were, to stop Ursus from burning my lord's books together with his own. When my lord realized that he would become no different, and could no longer bear him as he was, he dismissed him and let him go.

This then is a brief account of what I knew about this same Ursus, when he served my lord somewhat longer than the year [1584]. But to tell about all his past aberrations would take too long. The foregoing is true, however, as I can testify together with all those who served my lord at that time. Furthermore, I will bear this witness again, even in Ursus's presence. For the sake of greater authenticity I wrote this out with my own hand, signed it, and impressed my seal on it, below.

Done in Kassel, 23 May 1598 — Michael Walter with his own hand[27]

Witness: Paul Cordet

Notary summoned for this purpose

In transmitting a copy of Walter's affidavit to Kepler in his letter of 29 November/9 December 1599, Brahe commented:

> Later on this testimony was confirmed by Eric [Lange] himself at Magdeburg in the presence of a public notary. Moreover, whatever Ursus has elsewhere in that infamous publication, to the extent that Lange had some definite information about the matter, he testified that it was utterly false. With regard to twelve issues of this kind which were brought to his attention

> by being extracted from that infamous publication, he drew up what is called a public document, which you will see at another time. From this reaction you will judge the rest.[28]

Meanwhile, the Historian Royal of Denmark, Anders
72 Sörensen Vedel□ (1542-1616; Andreas Severini Velleius), who had been Brahe's tutor in 1562-1565, was engaged in compiling an official account of Danish affairs. He sent his report about Ursus to Brahe, who replied on 18 September 1599:

> But what you added about that brute from Dithmarschen was composed correctly by you. His stinking poem, which you sent, I was glad to receive. It is certain that Eric Lange, through the carelessness and imprudence with which he injures his own affairs too, created the opportunity for that foul beast to besmirch me with such grave insults since, without consulting me and against my will, he brought him with himself to my island [Hven]. But Lange was compelled for that reason to testify before a notary public about what he knew to be true in opposition to that infamous book even though he did this reluctantly. Everything was reported in parchment public documents, as they are called, written partly in Latin, partly in German, so that I might have them available for proof against him in Prague when I should decide to institute the suit, of course not by myself, since I deem him unworthy, but through a certain other plaintiff, hired at my expense. I had decided previously to do this. For it is a question of my honor and reputation, which I must guard even if I did not go to Prague. But shortly after my arrival, feeling guilty, he fled, abandoning his wife there, whom he had recently married, a notorious adulteress (a lid suited to the pot).[29] But when

72. Anders Sörensen Vedel (Andreas Severini Velleius, 1542-1616), tutor of Tycho Brahe, later Historian Royal of Denmark

the opportunity arises, he will have to be tracked down. When I am relieved to some extent from more pressing business, it will be the right time to drag that beast, wherever he may be hiding, into court. This too will not be difficult for me, whether this is to be accomplished in Prague or elsewhere. In this matter I have secretly inquired of the archbishop of Prague, a distinguished man descended from a famous family, whether he was aware that this infamous book was printed in Prague, since it is his duty to take notice of these things. But he excused himself, protesting that the book was printed without his knowledge. He wanted the author summoned to court and punished according to the laws, which he agreed that he would do.[30]

XXIV

A KEPLER-URSUS PLOT AGAINST BRAHE?

XXIV

A KEPLER-URSUS PLOT AGAINST BRAHE?

On 28 March 1600 Brahe wrote from Benátky to his friend Jan Jesenský (Jessenius, 1566-1621), the emperor's physician, in Prague as follows:

> A certain member of my household who is concerned about my affairs and whom I had recently at the court in Pilsen wrote that a certain leading councillor of our most clement lord, His Imperial Majesty, had indicated to him that a long time ago a certain Ursus of Dithmarschen had submitted to the councillors an appeal complaining about me. It was, however, rejected dishonorably, and drew a sharp rebuke. The person who furnished me this information added nothing further about the contents of this appeal. He left Pilsen for his native land, which is in Westphalia.[1] I do not expect him back within three or four months.
>
> Nevertheless it is important for me to know in due course what that shameless man dared to complain about me. All the time I have been in Bohemia I have done no harm to him in any way, not even by a little word, either by myself or through others. Yet I had previously endured the unbearable wrongs and insults

which he was not ashamed to pile up in that infamous book which he published against me in Prague three years ago (in the judgment of informed men, this age has hardly seen a more disgusting and more deceptive book).

Pursuing a special plan, however, and also distracted by more important affairs, at that time I kept quiet about everything, as if I did not know about these matters. Certainly, if Ursus came my way, I would not recognize him. Nor was it clear to me whether in this interval he was in Prague or somewhere else, since I did not consider it worthwhile to find out about him. Hence, were his excessive arrogance, buffoonery, and shameless lying not known to me in some other way, I could not marvel enough what he could submit to the Most Worthy Lord Councillors by way of a complaint against me, who have been so quiet and have troubled him with no vexation. For he has nothing which he says truthfully, unless he wishes to accomplish this result, that I should keep quiet. Heretofore I have disdained his far-fetched silliness. Yet perhaps at the proper time it must be thrown back at him. To be sure, he has thereby damaged my fame and reputation (which disregards a thousand such slanderous clamors) not as much as he has disclosed his impudent banter and clownish character, chockful of curses and insults, to the entire world and to all those who judge fairly, as establishing himself in his own judgment as a mouse. On the other hand, the Most Honorable Councillors were perhaps not unaware of the insincerity of his character and language. They did not accept the complaint, but rejected him with a rebuke.

Nevertheless there may still be a hidden suspicion that some of his complaints were

not unjustified, but that I or my associates gave him opportunities to do this. For you know that highly popular saying in the world: Make your insults tough, something always sticks. For the sake of our friendship, with whatever entreaties I can [muster], I ask you to be willing to turn every stone so that I may get hold of a copy of his petition, or if this cannot be done discreetly, at least acquaint myself with a summary of its contents. But if this cannot be acquired otherwise, I hope that you will familiarize yourself with it, whatever it is, through the Most Magnificent
73, 74 and Most Noble Lord Mecker[2]□□ (who is genuinely well disposed toward me, as I am convinced by indications that are not dubious, and as you too remarked when we were last in Prague at the same time). Thus not only he but you too will have accomplished something quite dear to me and far from useless, perhaps even indispensable, to make me strong enough hereafter to avert such crafty and unjustified accusations.

For this is what my present situation now demands to be done, since I am a foreigner here. I am not sustained, as I was previously in my native land, by the prestige of the nobility, and kinship and connections with the most outstanding men. Indeed, outside the Imperial Court here, I lead a sheltered life, unaware of what is being said about me anywhere at all. Nor do I in other respects willingly become involved in the affairs of others. On the contrary, I have time only for my own researches. I have enough to do to the best of my ability to honor the Sparta I have found, for the glory of the most excellent emperor and empire to be able to plan and carry out, by grace of the Supreme Being, those projects

73. Leonhard Helfried von Meggau (1577-1644), who carried out Emperor Matthias's order reappointing Kepler as Imperial Mathematician

74. Matthias, Holy Roman Emperor from 1612 to 1619

> which I trust will be useful and memorable to all posterity. But you, my very dear Jesenský, by reason of that friendship which unites us, understand everything enough, so that there is no need for further elaboration, and I am altogether confident that you will not disappoint my wishes in this regard. Be well, and greet the Most Honorable Mecker most courteously for me. Written with a hasty pen in the imperial castle in Benátky on [18/]28 March 1600.[3]

A week and a half later, during a nearly complete rupture with Kepler, on 29 March/8 April 1600, in the course of another letter to the emperor's physician, Brahe charged Jesenský:

> Meanwhile find out by a third or fourth hand whether Kepler is quietly endeavoring to provide Ursus too with some reproaches against me[4] (for how shall I have confidence in him any more?). Still, I am not at all worried by whatever he says, provided he speaks the truth.[5]

That is what Kepler did, to the best of his ability, in his *Defense of Tycho against Ursus*. He may never have known that Brahe once suspected him of allying himself with Ursus against Tycho.

XXV

BRAHE'S STATEMENT TO HÁYEK AGAINST URSUS

XXV

BRAHE'S STATEMENT TO HÁYEK AGAINST URSUS

Having been notified by Háyek's letter of 19/29 August 1591 that Ursus had been appointed Imperial Mathematician despite the accusation of plagiarism hurled at him by Brahe,[1] at first the proud Dane kept his peace. Then drafting a reply to a different letter from Háyek, Brahe dated it in 1591. But he left a blank space for the month and day to be filled in later.[2] Then on 14 March 1592 he added a postscript in which he told Háyek:

> I had definitely made up my mind not to say a word about that plagiarist and stealthy thief, since I deemed him unworthy of mention. But while this letter was waiting here [in Uraniburg] a day or two for the wind and boat to take it over to Copenhagen, in the meantime I also came across a second recent letter of yours in which you referred to that Ursus of Dithmarschen. I see that in both your letters you refer in the same way to the man whom I had accused of plagiarism. Indeed, in the later letter you somewhat implicitly excuse him, and praise his character to such an extent as though you doubted whether he should deservedly and flatly be called a plagiarist,

perhaps because he so cleared himself in your eyes with his crafty and cunning words. I am therefore compelled willy-nilly to write to you more openly and at greater length about this matter so that you may be better informed how the situation stands.

This Ursus of Dithmarschen was here seven or eight years ago (unless I am mistaken) in the company of my close friend Eric Lange, in whose service he was at that time. For fourteen days this same Eric together with certain other barons and noblemen whom he had brought with him lived with me in a jolly way, as is the custom. Then, sending them away, he settled down to philosophize with me. (For he is not ignorant of the liberal arts, and he loves them, especially Urania, our [astronomy]. You may apply this name [Urania] also to my sister, otherwise known as Sophia, now a young widow, since Eric is in the habit of calling her by this name. The facts themselves may prove that what I have said is not far from the truth, for he loved her and is arranging to marry her.)[3]

Tired of alcoholic liquor and wishing to be refreshed by our Urania, Eric began to ask, among other questions, whether some method would not be found by which the absurdity of the earth's motion introduced by Copernicus could be obviated, and the Ptolemaic complexity and cumbersomeness eliminated in such a way, however, that the heavenly phenomena should be completely and neatly satisfied. For Eric became aware that I was constructing some such edifice, since he had sometimes heard the opinion drop from my lips that neither this theory nor that one conforms to the truth, but a far more suitable and probable theory can be devised.

I am not in the habit of wishing to thwart my good friend Eric's wishes, as far as I can. But looking behind me, among the other servitors I noticed this Dithmarschian standing near the table and more than the others listening intently to our conversation. With a nod I signaled to Eric to send him away somewhere. Lest he understand the matter and return too quickly, at once we gave him a topic to be put in poetic form by himself, since he claimed to be something of a poet.

Meanwhile, taking a piece of chalk, I drew on the table for Eric both the Ptolemaic and Copernican speculations about the heavenly motions, and I exposed the absurdities of both of them. When he asked about any third more suitable scheme, in a general and concise way I also sketched for him and explained what I too had devised on this subject. Afterwards, as far as we could, we rubbed these things out (for they were drawn on a green cloth covering the table). But that nosy little Ursus smelled that we had concealed these things. Either from those traces which perhaps still remained on the tablecloth, or from a certain piece of paper which had been thrown away among other scraps in my library, where he used to be, or from one of my students who perhaps had learned about these matters, or finally from some other source, in his mind he formed some idea of my hypotheses.

Not long afterward, on account of his bungling, overbearing, and stupid conduct he was dismissed by Eric. Passing through Holstein, he went to Magdeburg. In the house of that very learned man, George Rollenhagen, the director of the local school, he made very many remarkable boasts about this invention of the hypotheses which he falsely claimed for himself. When he was asked certain questions about explaining the planetary retrogradations and stationary points by Rollenhagen, who is not unfamiliar with astronomy, he could not extricate himself. Hence Rollenhagen was quite sure that Ursus did not originate this innovation. He pointed this out not so long afterward in letters to the noble lord Heinrich Rantzau and to me. He was the first to expose this plagiarism long before that feeble and inadequate *Foundation* [*of Astronomy*], scraped together, or rather stolen, from various authors was too arrogantly laid down by that Bear.

During the many days when I indulged the spirit of social enjoyment, as I said, rather than the mind of Eric and my other noble guests, Ursus examined and secretly searched through many other of my papers here. He copied very many things and committed some to memory, which he later advertised as his own without blushing (since he has no sense of shame). Examples are what he has to say about simplifying the complicated computations of triangles through prosthaphaereses, about instruments, the sextant and the quadrant, about improving the positions of the fixed stars by comparing them with Venus and the sun, and other similar topics. For as far as the simplification of triangles is concerned, long ago I collaborated gladly and freely with Wittich, when he was here. What was discovered by him and also by me in this matter was communicated back and forth.

Afterward, Wittich returned to his native
land [Silesia].☐ From there he set out for the 75
illustrious lord William, Landgrave of Hesse,
where he stayed for some time. To the Landgrave's clockmaker, Jost Bürgi, an uneducat-

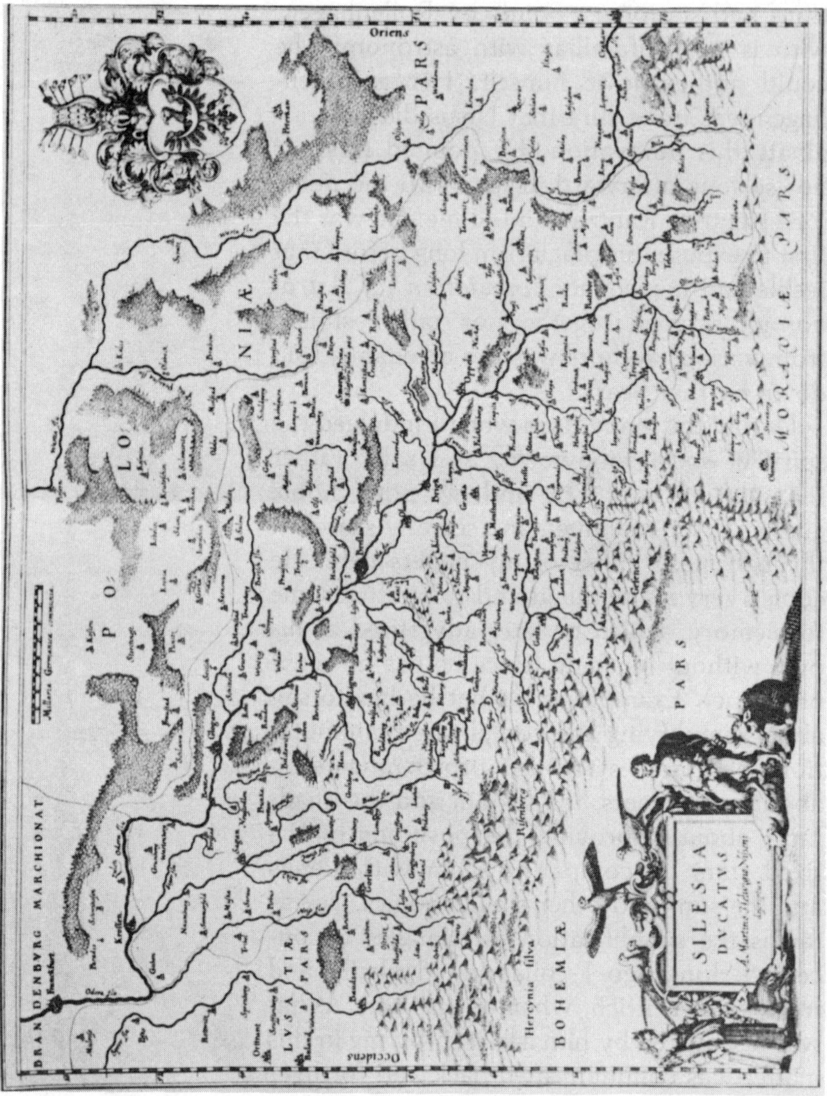

75. Silesia, by Martin Helwig of Neisse (1516-1574), who drew the first map of that region

ed but quite skillful mechanical craftsman, he divulged all the mysteries of the triangles which we had unraveled. Together with this information he disclosed there the construction of certain of my instruments and the method of refining [the measurements made by them] and the sights on them. As a result, the Landgrave soon had a sextant and quadrant constructed in imitation of mine (although Wittich did not discuss this too). Thereafter it was possible to perform more precise and more successful observations than previously, as you will learn from the astronomical letters exchanged by us.

After Wittich's departure, however, Ursus, who does not stay long in one residence and hiding-place (perhaps imitating the wild bears) also arrived in Kassel, presenting to the Landgrave my hypotheses as his own. They went to a lot of trouble to transpose these hypotheses to a planetarium. Although they had quite a qualified mechanical craftsman, they could not find the solution until the arrival of Rothmann, who added certain details to it in imitation of Copernicus. For Ursus had carried away only the more general features, as usually happens to sneaky crooks who out of fear and a twinge of conscience often leave untouched certain items which are far from useless. In Kassel, moreover, Ursus obtained a better grasp of the method of observing the heavenly bodies and improving their positions. To some extent he had seen this method here [in Uraniburg], it was expounded there [in Kassel] by Wittich, and was more fully explained in the letters exchanged by the Landgrave, his mathematician [Rothmann], and myself. What is most important (even though it turned out very badly), he obtained from

Jost Bürgi the compact demonstration and numerical solution of triangles which Wittich had imparted to Bürgi. In addition, [from Bürgi Ursus received] certain other material, in exchange for which he translated for him the whole of Copernicus into the German language.[4] These and other matters were reported to me by Christopher Rothmann not only by letters but also in person two years ago when he was sent here by the Landgrave for the purpose of inspecting my instruments.

Ursus, however, did not stay there [in Kassel] long. On the contrary, he soon crept and crawled to Strasbourg. What he had seen, learned, swiped here and at Kassel, for some time he propounded privately to students [in Strasbourg] as a way of making money. Finally, he did not fear to publish it under his own name with too presumptuous and high-sounding a title [*Foundation of Astronomy*], even though in most respects it was defective and imperfect. Some part of these scraps gathered from hither and yon in a certain novel and tasteless pattern he nominally dedicated to all the astronomers he had known.[5] I was the only one he passed over in silence (for this I congratulate myself because he did not besmirch my name with his thefts). Had others learned that he had some acquaintance with me, his deceit and plagiarism would be detected that much more quickly, since the greatest part of what he adduces there [in the *Foundation of Astronomy*], except insofar as he spoils these things or does not use them correctly, came out of my workshop.

However, in order that you may be sure that this is the situation, especially with regard to the arrangement of the hypotheses, I have enclosed the very sheet of paper that had been discarded (which I mentioned above). From this sheet he undoubtedly took this draft while he was here. As soon as I had been warned by Rollenhagen about this plagiarism, one of my students brought me this sheet which had been searched for among the other papers. He told me that this sheet lay exposed among other papers in my library while Ursus was here, so that he could easily derive from it what he published as his own. What he falsely claimed for himself was obtained from this source, as is sufficiently proved, if not otherwise, by the total inclusion of the solar orbit through some oversight in this old representation of Mars's orbit. That is the reason why this sheet had been discarded by me, perhaps because it was useless. In like manner, in Ursus's diagram these things are drawn incorrectly in imitation of that sheet. Everything else added on by Ursus is his idea of patchwork and has no firm connection with the subject. However, I want this sheet to be returned to me without fail.

Gellius Sascerides, who was mentioned above[6] and who was in my household eight years, was on his way from here to Italy, spent some time in Germany, and then went to Strasbourg. There he found Ursus bragging about his *Foundation*, put together from the labors of others. Gellius told Ursus to his face that he falsely attributed the invention of this hypothesis to himself. It was entirely my own, and Gellius had known it for some years previously in my house. That gross error concerning Mars's orbit totally surrounding the sun's in Ursus's diagram is enough of an indication that he did not understand these basic dispositions, not to mention that he could not be the originator of this innovation. Gellius also ob-

> jected that very many other things had been swiped from me. Since Ursus is stuffed with insolent cunning, he was not afraid to swear falsely that he did not take this hypothesis from me. Nevertheless he was compelled by Gellius to admit that he did not understand the hypothesis correctly and drew Mars's orbit incorrectly in it. How then, I ask, was it possible for him to originate what had been devised by someone else, when he did not correctly understand it, indeed rather distorted it? It is easy at another time to add something to what has been discovered.

Here Brahe implies that Ursus attributed the daily rotation to the earth, which remained stationary in the Tychonic system, otherwise simply repeated by Ursus, except for the Mars-sun intersection.

> Gellius wrote me letters about this matter not only from Strasbourg but also afterwards from Italy. I have enclosed them herein, but they are to be returned to me safe and sound. From them you will learn beyond any doubt that the situation is [as I have described it].

These letters from Gellius to Brahe have not survived.

> Gellius is a young man, who has already passed his thirtieth year [having been born on 3 March 1562]. Not only is he excellently educated in various disciplines [he went to Italy to study medicine, but took his doctoral degree at the University of Basel in 1593. He taught medicine at the University of Copenhagen from 1603 until his death on 9 November 1612] but he is also endowed with a sound character and exceptional seriousness. In particular, more than anyone else he is extremely sensitive to the truth, the love of which he has often heard praised by me in the highest degree.

If there is nothing else to prove that Ursus took this hypothesis by whatever trickery from my innovation, whereas I did not borrow it from his hodgepodge scraped together from hither and yon, this conclusion will emerge quite clearly from the printing of my *Recent Phenomena in the Celestial World*, Book II, long before his rhapsodical *Foundation* was published. When it was issued, I had previously devised these hypotheses, being impelled to this result by the heavenly phenomena themselves, considered in their simplicity. At that time I had decided to hold this hypothesis in reserve for a complete work on the revival of astronomy. But I was afraid of Ursus and of someone else, a Scot.[7] Having learned this hypothesis from conversations here, the Scot later expounded it privately to his pupils in Rostock. Yet he did not deny, as Ursus did, with sincere intention that the innovation was mine, and he admitted that he had conceived this theory here in my house. This, I say, and similar developments are what I was afraid of when I prudently decided to insert these matters in Book II [Chapter 8], putting them ahead of the rest for a definite reason.

As far as triangles are concerned, you will see in the proper place in some of my Books several relevant precepts which I wrote down very many years ago for my students to have a more convenient method of astronomical computation by this means. A copy of these precepts was open for inspection on the individual tables of our library (so that absolutely everybody might have his own copy of them available). Hence it was very easy for Ursus, playing the crafty parasite for so many days, to dip into them. Yet he could hardly obtain the geometrical proofs of these precepts in this way, since I had kept them separately among certain of my more important writings. Later on, he acquired the proofs at Kassel from the Landgrave's craftsman through the opportunity which I mentioned [Wittich's instruction of Bürgi]. In fact, I have many other sheets, written with his own hand, which he copied secretly here and had made up his mind to steal together with the rest. Yet he always said openly that everything he saw here was unnecessary and unimportant. He was not ashamed to brag that with three sticks he would do more things more correctly and more quickly than I with all my instruments and machines. He called this the tridendronic art. I don't know whether he understood these to be the three limbs of the gallows which I arranged to have painted for this purpose in his portrait, together with the poem that follows. If so, let him have this method of observing the stars for himself. Certainly nobody will envy him his possession of it, but will rather feel sorry for him. The poem read as follows:

He who first founded the art
of the three sticks
Was to be beheld with this face and beard.
No wonder that darkness is signified
by the appearance of his features,
Since he fits the three sticks so neatly.
But he will have to be strung up,
whether some day perhaps
Tied up to them or suffering
a bondsman's fate.

Indeed, in rebuttal of his denial with no proper excuse that he copied most of my papers here without my knowledge, I still have a whole bundle of them which he furtively wrote

> here with his own hand and was engaged in taking away with him. For I had persuaded his master Eric to arrange to have them taken back again secretly at night from him, buried in wine and sleep,[8] some day before he left. However, the lad who was supposed to carry out this retaliation was not clever enough nor did he find the purloined materials. In like manner Ursus himself did not snatch in its entirety everything he wanted to carry away, whether you apply this to his brain or his hand. He may, however, persist in his spitefulness by not confessing his plagiarism and disclaiming it, but corruptly and falsely excusing it. In that case I shall proceed to have him publicly accused there [in Prague], convicted, and punished as he deserves in accordance with the laws (unless I spare him on account of the indifferent knowledge of mathematics which he has acquired). For I have quite good reasons to pursue this vengeance (if I wished to). Not only did he dishonestly snatch from me certain things created by my many exertions, efforts, and expenses, and falsely attribute them to himself. But he also tried to impair my reputation and honor at Kassel in the court of the Landgrave and perhaps elsewhere by his insolent and malicious lies as much as he could, as may be seen in Christopher Rothmann's letter near the bottom of page 33 in the part of the volume of *Astronomical Letters* which was sent to you.

Parts of Brahe's *Astronomical Letters*, first published as a whole in 1596, were distributed earlier to friends such as Háyek.

> Not even with a little word have I deemed it worthwhile to reply to this nonsense, because by themselves insults, falsehoods, scurrility in

the end lead to absurdities. Nor should you allow him to write anything to me, since I consider his cunning and worthless excuses as quite transparent and suspect in other regards. I have come to know the man more than is necessary, not however as you still judge him: humane, simple, benevolent, frugal, pure, clean (if you understand this through its opposite, perhaps you will grasp my meaning more accurately: "a snake lurks in the grass").[9] I do not doubt that that shrewmouse will soon betray himself by such a proof as to leave no difficulty in his being understood by you too. I shall add no more, although other things are clear to me about his cunning and treacherous character. For he is not worth having even those things written about him which I have already said, although they are true enough and more than enough. Moreover, I want you not to disclose these things, but to keep this information shared only by Kurtz and yourself, unless some exigency exerts pressure. For by himself he was previously quite infamous and, unless he adopts other ways, hereafter he will make himself more infamous, so that there is no need for him to be made more infamous, by others.

Written in Uraniburg
14 March 1592[10]

XXVI

KEPLER, MAESTLIN, BRAHE, AND HERWART

XXVI

KEPLER, MAESTLIN, BRAHE, AND HERWART

From Graz on 9/19 September 1600 Kepler reported to Maestlin:

> Most renowned teacher, on 1 June [1600] I departed from Benátky for Graz. I left the negotiations hanging in the balance. Decisions by the [imperial] court are slow. With the help of very excellent interventions, I could have accepted a salary in the service of the emperor. But I was deterred by the experiences of those awarded magnificent salaries who extract barely half with immense difficulty. Accordingly it was agreed between Tycho and me that I would wait in Graz for the emperor's letter whereby, while retaining my Styrian salary, I would move to Bohemia for two years; my traveling expenses would be sent together with this letter....
>
> On 1 August [1600] for more than a thousand citizens and clergymen of the Estates in this city, including me, permanent exile was decreed, effective in forty-five days [or less than a week after Kepler wrote this letter]. All personal goods have become very cheap; no money is exchanged among people except Hun-

garian small change; all property is minutely inventoried. You may imagine all the other evils. I reported this to Prague [in a letter that has not been preserved]. Tycho answers [in a letter that also has not been preserved] that by word of mouth he recommended me to the emperor and I was approved; only the letter concerning this matter is awaited.

But because their plans are thrown into confusion by the termination of my Styrian salary (since I have given it up because I am about to go to another homeland and voluntarily look for another employer), Brahe strongly urges me to forget about Württemberg [where Kepler was hoping for a position at the University of Tübingen] and come to Bohemia as quickly as possible. I remain undecided. Yet I am planning to go to Linz with my family and, leaving them there, to proceed by myself to Prague. While I am there, I shall find out what salary will be awarded me, and what hope there will be of extracting it, to the extent granted me by divine grace....

I married a wife from a prosperous family, all her relatives being in the same situation. But their entire wealth is in land, which is very cheap, indeed, it cannot be sold. Everybody longs for it, since it carries no price tag. For a warning has been issued by the ruler that property not sold within the forty-five days may not be leased by anybody to any agent. These are indeed harsh terms. Yet I would not have believed that it is so sweet to suffer losses and insults, to abandon homes, lands, friends, and country, with a scanty band of brethren, for the sake of religion, for the honor of Christ. But if martyrdom and loss of life are calibrated on a definite scale, so that the greater the damage, the greater the joy, it is easy even to die for one's religion.[1]

Fortunately for mankind, Kepler did not find it necessary to die for his religion. Deprived of his employment and driven away from his home, he joined Brahe for nearly four months from 5 February to 1 June 1600, with an interruption of about three weeks. During this stay in Bohemia, Kepler told Brahe about his letter to Herwart concerning Ursus. Since Kepler had no copy of the letter to show to Brahe, on 28 August 1600, the day on which Brahe informed Kepler in Graz about his plan to compile a book condemning Ursus, Brahe also wrote to Herwart in part as follows:

> In Benátky this past spring Johannes Kepler, the distinguished mathematician of Styria, was with me. I was informed by him that you too are in contact with him through correspondence. Among other things he told me that he once wrote you something about my hypotheses, which are a subject of controversy. He showed that they were found neither in Copernicus nor in Apollonius of Perga, as is claimed by a certain individual (who died fourteen days ago). By definite proofs Kepler concluded that they belong to no other person, but are my own. In the friendliest way I therefore ask you please to let me see Kepler's letter for a little while, or at least to have the words concerning this matter extracted from it and verified by a note in your handwriting testifying that the copy is accurate. By the earliest courier returning here from you, please send it, whatever it is, to the agent (as he is called) of your ruler, to be forwarded to me. In this way you will have done me a very great favor. For at the present time there is some urgent need why I would want this to happen, about which you will be informed on another occasion.[2]

According to the editor of GW *14*, Brahe addressed this request to Herwart "out of a certain mistrust of Kepler."[3] But no such feeling was involved. What Brahe wanted from Herwart was an authentication of what Kepler had written about Ursus, because Brahe wanted to incorporate a legal document of this sort in his anti-Ursus volume. On 11 September 1600 Herwart replied to Brahe from Munich in part as follows:

> When I returned home today, I found your letter written from Prague on 28 August, new style. In it you ask among other things for the earliest possible transmission to you of what Joannes Kepler previously wrote to me about your hypotheses. He is of course an outstanding mathematician. Not only in that capacity but also on account of his sincerity, I like him extremely well. For that reason I would not want to offend him in any way or under any circumstance. However, you write that the individual who had claimed those hypotheses for himself is now dead. Therefore, not only for the sake of the existing situation but also in view of the friendship which you feel for me, I am completely convinced that this communication will not displease my friend Kepler. I have accordingly decided to honor your request. On 30 May of last year, 1599, Kepler wrote as follows.[4]

The letter sent by Kepler to Herwart on 30 May 1599 still survives.[5] It was not sent to Brahe by Herwart. Instead, he marked the desired material by heavily drawing two large signs for a parenthesis as a guide for his copyist. This extract, certified by Herwart in his own hand as a faithful copy, was then sent to Brahe. In the course of a long letter written from Prague on 8 February 1601 while he was suffering from a fever, Kepler told Maestlin:

> On account of this illness of mine I am doing

nothing but writing against Ursus (who died last summer). In that regard I deal with nothing but what concerns science. My greatest interest is in antiquity, and in explaining the beliefs of the ancients. Hence the treatment will hardly be mathematical, but only semantic. If anything appeals to you, help it along, for I shall be glad to receive advice, especially in the problems proposed by Ursus for solution. I am vexed that up to the present time you do not write.[6]

On 9/19 October 1600 Maestlin had written to Kepler in part:

> With regard to what you recently wrote about publishing my letters, I ask you not to do so. For I wrote them as a friend to a friend, not acquired at length by an exchange of correspondence, as though he had previously been a stranger. But if the thought had ever crossed my mind that they would be published some day, I would have written much more carefully. They were written as the pen dictated, for I was writing not to others, but to you, who would be the honest interpreter of all the words, even those written crudely. It was enough for me that you understood my meaning, however the words were written. Yet if we have to talk within earshot of the world, that is different from the conversation of personal friends. I disapprove of the intention of those who are so quick to publish the letters of personal friends writing about personal matters. Thus I believe that I would do you no favor if I should likewise publish your letters (in which you sometimes mention those persons, for instance, whom you suspect of having obstructed your astronomical work in the court of our ruler)[7] [the duke of Württemberg].

Kepler replied that the letter written by Maestlin in Tübingen on 9/19 October 1600, the very day on which he arrived in Prague, was received by him on 9 December, new style. A week later, on 6/16 December 1600, Kepler answered Maestlin:

> If I ever wrote to you about publishing your letters, I am greatly astonished that the Kepler of an hour is so different from the Kepler of all hours. To my knowledge, I never had the idea of doing it; that practice never pleased me; nor do I recall the words. And I ask you to send me the words, time, place, or rather the entire letter.[8]

Since Kepler had written no such letter, Maestlin could not have sent it back to him. Maestlin may well have been annoyed that he had mistakenly accused Kepler of wanting to publish his private letters. Being unwilling to admit his error, however, Maestlin chose not to write to Kepler. Hence, when the latter informed Maestlin about his appointment as Imperial Mathematician as Brahe's successor, he began his letter of 10/20 December 1601 as follows:

> Your silence for so long a time absolutely convinces me that you have imagined as a reason for keeping quiet the charge with which you reproached me in your most recent letter.[9]

And toward the close of the same letter, Kepler reverted to this theme:

> For the sake of our studies, I beseech you not to be so completely silent. If I wrote that I would publish your letters (I still cannot remember having done so), I certainly am sorry; I pledge that I will not do so.[10]

Kepler's appeal elicited no response from Maestlin until 1605.

XXVII

KEPLER'S "QUARREL BETWEEN TYCHO AND URSUS OVER HYPOTHESES"

76. Brahe's son-in-law (1576-1623), "Franz Ganzneb, called Tengnagel," as he signed his report on 12 December 1621 concerning his father-in-law's manuscripts and instruments (GW, XIX, 368, #7, 103); in Kepler's contract with Brahe's heirs, signed in Prague on 29 October 1612, Kepler had called him "Tengnagel of Campe," presumably Kamp on the northwest coast of Holland (GW, XIX, 191/12-13)

XXVII

KEPLER'S "QUARREL BETWEEN TYCHO AND URSUS OVER HYPOTHESES"

In his letter of 8 February 1601, as we just saw,
Kepler informed Maestlin: "I am doing nothing but
writing against Ursus." He did so then at the request
of Brahe. But in March of the previous year his "opinion of Brahe's hypotheses, which a certain[1] Nicholas
Ursus of Dithmarschen presumes to claim for himself"
had been sought by Franz Tengnagel□ (1576-1623), 76
Brahe's future son-in-law. When Kepler's father-in-
law died, Kepler wanted to convert his wife's share of
the estate into cash that could be taken out of the
country. Hence he returned for a few months to Graz,
where on 31 May 1601 he wrote to his wife Barbara,
who had remained behind in Prague, asking (in a secret code) whether Elizabeth Brahe was perceptibly
pregnant.[2] She married Tengnagel on 7/17 June 1601,[3]
and their child was born on 28 September 1601.[4] Present at the wedding was the astronomer who started
the study of variable stars, David Fabricius (1564-
1617), also well known as an astrologer. For that
reason Tengnagel wanted Fabricius to cast his horoscope and send it to Kepler.[5] To explain why he wrote
the "Quarrel between Tycho and Ursus over Hypotheses," Kepler said that Tengnagel "was eager to

know these things better."[6] But in March 1600 Tengnagel undoubtedly approached Kepler at the instigation of Brahe, who kept the original draft of the "Quarrel" to be used in his contemplated lawsuit against Ursus. Although the original is lost, a copy, not in Kepler's handwriting, is still preserved in the Austrian National Library in Vienna. In the copy the "Quarrel" is preceded by a preliminary statement (presumably drafted by Brahe) to the effect that

> if Ursus could not convince the better informed [that he was the originator of the new hypotheses] at least he would induce the belief that these were not devised by Tycho, but were taken from Martianus Capella, Copernicus or Apollonius of Perga. All this is compactly and rigorously refuted here by Kepler, an outstanding astronomer, thoroughly familiar with Ptolemy and Copernicus. In the same spirit, before he knew Tycho face to face, to that noble and distinguished man, Johann George Herwart of Hohenburg, chancellor of the provincial Estates of Bavaria, who posed this question, he had also written a letter which can be considered at the proper time and adduced in support of the truth.[7]

Having received from Herwart the section concerning Ursus in Kepler's letter of 20/30 May 1599, Brahe filed it with Kepler's "Quarrel between Tycho and Ursus over Hypotheses," which began as follows:

> When a certain scholar [Herwart] asked me to put my opinion of this matter in writing for him, I replied in general as follows, as far as it comes to mind [Kepler had to rely on his memory, no copy of his 20/30 May 1599 letter to Herwart being available]. In the first place, I did not conceal my anger at Ursus, who disgracefully abused my letter by publishing it without consulting me. Accordingly I bade the scholar to consider whether I was being

carried away by my feelings. Secondly, I did not want to pass judgment on insults before a man in public affairs.

However, with regard to the question which one of the two swipes the other's hypotheses, even though I myself adopt a different hypothesis [Copernicanism], nevertheless Ursus seems guilty of the crime as charged. The grounds were as follows. Ursus admits that in Rollenhagen's house he showed a sheet of paper brought from Denmark. He calls this an intellectual theft, and advises Tycho to learn how to protect his possessions better hereafter. Ursus acknowledges that he did not originate this hypothesis, except insofar as he made the earth turn in a daily rotation. He declares, finally, that he extracted the hypotheses from the same source as Tycho, since they are available explicitly in Copernicus and Ptolemy.

This last contention is false, however, because these hypotheses do not exist in the places mentioned. Therefore, from this misstatement and from the first three correct statements: that he is not the originator of the hypothesis, that he has the hypothesis from the same source as Tycho, and that he swiped Tycho's sheet of paper containing this hypothesis, the following inference is derived, as it were, from certain first principles: Tycho's hypothesis was swiped by Ursus and claimed as his own.

Tycho's hypothesis, however, is not present in Copernicus and Ptolemy, as is clear from the distortion of the passages cited by Ursus, which we shall review one by one.

Book I, Chapter 10. In this entire chapter Copernicus discreetly approaches the exposition and absolute inevitability of his hypothesis by a gradual development from the opportunity provided by Martianus Capella.

For according to Capella, Venus and Mercury have opposite circles around the body of the sun, whence he apparently relates the centers of their spheres to the sun.[8] And then Copernicus proceeds:

> Hence, if anyone (meaning: if I, Copernicus) seized this opportunity to link Saturn, Jupiter, and Mars also to that center, he will not be mistaken, as is shown by the regular pattern of their motions,[9]

and as will be shown by this work of mine, in which I have constructed this regular pattern on the basis of such a hypothesis. Here Ursus pretends that Copernicus is talking about some modification of his hypothesis. Yet Copernicus has not yet explained his hypothesis, but with these very words is now preparing his approach to expounding it. Did Copernicus see what Tycho saw, that the sun, moving with a yearly motion, could nevertheless remain the center for the five planets? (But Copernicus could not see this, since he believed in the reality of the spheres.)[10] For had Copernicus seen this, why would he have said a little later on that either alternative must be true: either the ratio of the earth's orbit to the sphere of the fixed stars is nil, or that innumerable multitude of spheres is accepted in agreement with the ancients?[11] For neither alternative is necessary for anybody who agrees with Tycho.

Book III, Chapter 25. Here Ursus did not understand Copernicus, or pretended not to, with a dishonorable intention. This cannot be doubted by anybody who understands Copernicus. He is talking about the theory of the sun, to which this Book [III] is devoted. Ursus, however, thinks that he is talking about the entire range of the hypotheses and the mutual compatibility of the parts of the universe.

To clarify the matter, I shall draw two diagrams, one of which will depict Copernicus's first idea. But the other will show the variation Copernicus is talking about in this passage. [In the first diagram] let the center of the earth's eccentric be A, namely, the sun. Let B be the epicycle which, like the eccentric, completes an annual motion, but in the opposite direction and with a slightly shorter period, so that this difference gives rise to the apogee's displacement. Let C be the center of the second epicycle, traversed by the earth in 3434 years, as a result of which the shift in the eccentricity occurs. In the words cited by Ursus, Copernicus says that this model can be changed in such a way that A is the center of the universe, but not of the sun's actual body. Around A, the earth in D revolves in an annual motion (note carefully that the earth still revolves). Let the sun be in C, and move on the epicycles B,C, but so slowly that it makes no perceptible advance in a year. For in relation to the fixed stars, epicycle B revolves in 25,000 years, and epicycle C in 3434 years. Now read Copernicus, and you will see how far away Copernicus is from Ursus's interpretation. One of them is talking about onions, the other about garlic.

Book V, Chapter 35. In this passage Copernicus mentioned Apollonius and said the same things about him as Ptolemy [did in the *Syntaxis*], Book XII, Chapter 1. With regard to this passage, as it seems to me, somebody smarter than Ursus advised him that something Tychonian is present in Ptolemy under the name of Apollonius. Ursus, however, being too glib in these matters, is satisfied with what Copernicus derives from the same Ptolemy. For especially with a view to fabricating his misrepresentation, it was convenient for Ursus to seize upon what is completely missing from this passage, since previously he did not have the time to consult Ptolemy.

There are two forms of Apollonius's theorem, one of which is discussed by Copernicus, and by Ursus, following him. It has no more to do with Ursus's thinking or Tycho's hypothesis than Copernicus himself [has in the passage analyzed just] above. The accompanying diagram explains the idea. A is the stationary earth. BD is the planet's concentric, which revolves in 30 years in the case of Saturn, and so on. For Apollonius, believing that the planets are subject to no irregularity other than that which is linked to the sun and produces the retrogradations, neglected to make BD eccentric. The epicycle FG produces the commuting motion. Now from the earth's center A draw the line AG intersecting the epicycle in H,G, so that EG:AH as the concentric's motion CE is to the epicycle's [motion] FG. Then, as Apollonius proved, the planet becomes stationary in points H,G. This first form of the theorem, mentioned by Copernicus, Ptolemy, and Ursus, has absolutely nothing to do with Tycho's hypothesis, and indeed is concerned with entirely different goals.

Had Ursus seen the second form, he would have mingled heaven and earth with delirious joy. It goes like this. A is the center of the earth, universe, and planetary spheres. B is the sun in its sphere. CD is any planet's concentric, revolving with the solar sphere B and in the same direction. ED is the planet's large epicycle, whose center C encircles the earth, with that epicycle's westward motion [producing] the commuting motion. Through this assumption Apollonius again seeks the line determining the stationary points, as before.

This form is so arranged that some clever person can derive the Tychonian hypothesis from it, but not without hard work. Indeed, it [would be] infinitely harder than [deriving the Tychonian hypothesis] from the Copernican theory. For in the first place no hint, no trace of the Tychonian hypothesis is evident and conspicuous in that second form, since the author's aim is directed toward establishing the stationary points, and not at all toward arranging the parts of the universe. Secondly, the center of the planets is located not in the sun, but in the earth. Thirdly, all the planets are not considered at the same time, but individual planets separately. Fourthly, every planet has its own geocentric sphere. Fifthly, what Tycho calls the planet's sphere is present in Apollonius (even if an appropriate modification has been introduced) and it is called the large epicycle. Sixthly, Apollonius does not say that the sun and the centers of those large epicycles are carried on one concentric around the earth, but he does say that they are carried in a uniform revolution simultaneously. Seventhly, in Apollonius, Mars's sphere does not intersect the sun's sphere. Eighthly, in Apollonius's surviving writings it is not clear that the annual parallax provided the opportunity to investigate the proportion of the spheres. Ninthly, the eastward motion of that large epicycle in Apollonius, or of the sphere in Tycho, is much shorter for the former, because its period is a year, give or take a little, whereas in Tycho for Saturn it is thirty years, Jupiter twelve, Mars about two. Hence it is clear that Ursus did not understand Copernicus, Ptolemy, Apollonius, nor can the Tychonian hypothesis be derived so easily from Apollonius.

The foregoing was written by Johannes Kepler, the mathematician of Styria, for the sake of the noble youth Franz Tengnagel[12] who, as an employee of Tycho, was eager to know these things better.

In the year 1600, in the month of March.[13]

XXVIII

THE DEATH OF URSUS

XXVIII

THE DEATH OF URSUS

Not long after Kepler returned to Graz, on 25 June 1600 he wrote Brahe a letter that has not been preserved. Tycho did not answer it right away because, as he told Kepler,

> I did not want to write anything to you before the entire matter was settled in accordance with your wishes, and the letter was drafted by which you would be called here honorifically. But in the meantime your second letter [of 10 August 1600, that also has not been preserved] arrives a few days ago. What it says in the beginning is not very different from your earlier letter [of 25 June 1600]. But toward the end it announces a certain unexpected calamity which undermines to no small extent not only your previous plans but also my own. For I understand from it that your Styrian salary has been withdrawn from you, as from certain others also, and in addition you have been condemned to exile unless you obey the decree that has been promulgated there.[1]

This decree required Protestants like Kepler to leave Styria if they did not convert to Catholicism. In a postscript to this letter of 28 August 1600 Brahe told Kepler that in his (lost) letter of 10 August 1600

> You also added that you intend to refute the mathematical sections in that infamous publication of Ursus, in so far as they are not correct. I trust that you will do so. In particular, however, I would like you to rebut even more clearly and more fully than you have previously Ursus's distorted and dishonest objections to my invention of the new hypothesis, namely, that it was derived from Copernicus or Apollonius of Perga, and not to think it disagreeable to ascribe the new hypothesis to me, as is right, just as you did before with demonstrable reasoning.[2]

Kepler had dealt briefly with the "Quarrel between Tycho and Ursus over Hypotheses" while he was in Benátky, whither he had been escorted from Prague on 5 February 1600 by Tengnagel. During the month of March he wrote the "Quarrel" in direct response to a request by Tengnagel, who was undoubtedly complying with a suggestion of Brahe. On 25 July 1600 Herwart expressed his wonder to Kepler "how Tycho and Ursus, so near each other, can function."[3] As if in answer to this question, in the postscript of his 28 August 1600 letter to Kepler, Brahe went on to report:

> I began legal action against Ursus after I came here to Prague [after 10 July 1600] on the understanding that I have to remain here for some time and there is danger in delay, since he was seriously ill. I asked His Imperial Majesty (although certain persons[4] caused as long a delay as they could) to appoint four commissioners, two barons and two doctors of jurisprudence, to make the decision in this matter. When Ursus was asked by my emissaries to retract what he had written, he refused but instead proceeded to trial. Yet at the very hour

> when the summons was to be served on him,
> it happened that he died.[5]

On 28 August 1600, the day on which Brahe wrote his letter and postscript to Kepler, he sent a message also to Herwart, in which he referred to Ursus's "death 14 days ago."[6] Although Brahe's reference to Ursus's death on 15 August 1600 was printed in F *1*: 232/26↑-25↑, F *1*: 657/14↑ mistakenly said that "Ursus died in the year 1599, almost two years before Tycho." After Tycho's death on 24 October 1601, the funeral oration was pronounced on 4 November 1601 by Jesenský. In his *Life and Death of Tycho Brahe* Jesenský said about Ursus:

> A few short years ago a certain clever and learned man, lacking probity and honesty, published a foul and infamous book against this most outstanding man, the sort of book not seen in antiquity nor perhaps ever to be seen by posterity. It would not have been enough for that defamer to commit a literary plagiarism and falsely publicize as his own discovery the hypothesis devised by Tycho in Uraniburg. With countless insults and as many lies he would also have rendered suspect, if not dishonored, in the minds of others a man of ancient lineage, loftiest erudition, and most blameless life together with his most reputable family. There surely would have been a legal action against him, as even now it has begun, had not death struck that wild beast with special kindness and saved him from a thoroughly deserved punishment.[7]

From Jesenský's funeral oration, the first comprehensive report on Ursus somehow drew an uncertain inference that he fled from Prague and died "soon thereafter in the same year 1599, unless I am mistaken."[8] These closing words (*nisi fallor*) were disregarded when the report was paraphrased in F *1*:

218/6-7. Thus the report's uncertain inference was turned into F's categorical (mis)statement that Ursus died in 1599, contradicting Brahe's precise date, 15 August 1600. In his 28 August 1600 postscript Brahe told Kepler about his plans to pursue Ursus beyond the grave:

> Nevertheless I shall persist in the action I started, since the lawsuit was already joined, as it were. This is not entirely a personal action, but it is also a real action, on account of his infamous book, which speaks forever in the place of its author. My purpose is to obtain legal protection for myself and my family from the insults with which it abounds. The Most Illustrious Emperor has already ordered the archbishop [of Prague] to seek out all the copies which are found here and have them burned, and to punish the printer.[9]

A month earlier the archbishop had written to Brahe:

> With regard to the book of which you sent me a copy, and of which Nicholas Reimers Ursus says he is the author, I cannot find out who printed it in this city without my approval. But I shall take care to have the printer tracked down and, if he is found, to have others view him as an appropriate example, and to seize whatever copies he has. But since Ursus is under the jurisdiction of the Most Illustrious Court Marshal, you will be able to call on him and request him officially to demand that Ursus identify the printer and hand over whatever copies he has. In whatever way I can and should, I shall not fail to assist in this matter.
> Prague, in the archbishop's residence
> 27 July 1600[10]

Neither the archbishop nor the Court Marshal could find out who printed Ursus's *Astronomical Hypo-*

theses, and he has not yet been identified. In his 28 August 1600 postscript Brahe went on to tell Kepler that the Imperial Vice-Chancellor Rudolph

> Corraduc has promised the promulgation of an imperial decree prohibiting the book throughout the entire [Holy Roman] Empire, and declaring it banned as an infamous and scurrilous book.[11]

The decree was enforced so rigorously that very few copies of Ursus's *Astronomical Hypotheses* survived. Even the author of the most important biography of Brahe could not locate a copy.[12] In his 28 August 1600 postscript Brahe explained how he would like Kepler to participate in his anti-Ursus project:

> I have decided hereafter to publish this entire proceeding, together with the commissioners' decision and His Imperial Majesty's decree, in a special book which will expand to a moderate size. I shall, God willing, do this with His Most Clement Majesty's consent and Corraduc's approval already vouchsafed me. In the second part of the book I shall reply to the questions which are mathematical and concern the hypotheses. That is why I should also like to have your views of these matters soon. Or if (as I hope) you come here as quickly as possible, the matter can wait until you arrive.[13]

To his friend and relative, Holger Rosenkrantz (1574-1642), Brahe wrote a letter from Benátky on 3 June 1600. But he kept it for two months until it could be taken safely to Denmark by Longberg. In a postscript hastily added on 3 August from Prague, Brahe reported that the emperor, having stayed in Pilsen three-quarters of a year to avoid the plague, had returned to Prague and summoned Brahe there. In Prague, Brahe learned that

> the man from Dithmarschen, the author of the infamous book against me, is fatally ill, in part worn out by very serious sicknesses, in part worried about that crime and fearful of punishment. For a long time now I have wanted him cited in court for those horrible wrongs and insults, with which you are familiar, and judged by law. But since on account of the plague the imperial court has been scattered now almost a whole year, this could not be done heretofore. Therefore I am now urging the institution of the suit, since this is a personal action and there is danger in delay. I have already asked His Imperial Majesty to designate from among his councillors certain commissioners to master everything about this easy case and arrive at a final verdict. What this will turn out to be, you will learn in the end.[14]

Ursus was discussed also by Rollenhagen in a (lost) letter to Brahe. About a month after the postscript on this subject in his 28 August 1600 letter to Kepler, Brahe replied to Rollenhagen on 16/26 September 1600 in part as follows:

> What you added about Ursus turned out almost exactly as you seemed to predict. For whether he was attacked [by syphilis] in the French camp, to which he was accustomed, or by asthma and consumption, or rather by both conditions, he died six weeks ago. This occurred at the very hour when he was to be served with the indictment of the Imperial Commissioners, whom I had procured to judge him and his infamous publication. For as soon as the emperor returned from Pilsen, □ he
> most graciously summoned me here to Prague 77
> [from Benátky], as you know. As soon as I arrived, I was told that Ursus was dangerously

77. Pilsen, where Emperor Rudolph II fled to escape the plague raging in Prague

> ill. I sent him two doctors of jurisprudence together with a public notary to ask whether he was willing to retract that malicious publication, chockful of insults. At the same time I prepared the main items of the insults to be read to him. He would not admit most of them, even though they were found spelled out on the pages indicated in his publication. Nevertheless he refused to recant. On the contrary, he submitted everything to the decision of the judges. Consequently, more than happy when I saw this, I most humbly obtained from the emperor the appointment of four commissioners to decide the case by law. Two of them were barons, Christopher von Schleunitz and Ernfried von Minckwitz. The other two were doctors of jurisprudence from His Majesty's councillors. But the defendant died.[15]

Brahe clearly implies that Ursus died in Prague, as against the erroneous inference from Jesenský's funeral oration that the place where Ursus died is uncertain.[16] Brahe's letter to Rollenhagen of 16/26 September 1600 continued:

> The indictment was not read to Ursus before
> he died. The case was suspended until a new
> decree should arrive, as will happen soon, I
> trust. I am only waiting for the return of my at-
> torney in this case, a certain Johannes Fritzsch,
> doctor of law, who left for Bautzen□ in Lu- 78
> satia. For this is not merely a personal action,
> but also a real action on account of the pub-
> lication of the book which speaks forever in
> the place of its author. Therefore I must pro-
> ceed against it. All the insults with which it
> abounds must be disclosed, refuted, and con-
> demned. Afterwards they must be divulged in
> another published book containing the full
> proceedings and all the counterproofs. There
> will be added His Imperial Majesty's decree

78. Bautzen, Caspar Peucer's birthplace, after a drawing by Dilich

> declaring that infamous book invalid throughout the entire empire or, as they say, annulled. The Most Reverend Archbishop of Prague has already been charged by the emperor to notify the printer, have all the copies sought out, as many as are found in Prague, and have them consigned to the flames. Had the author lived a while longer, he would have been sentenced, as I learned from the commissioners, to be branded in infamy, and beheaded or quartered according to Bohemian law. To me, however, the question was not so much destroying his person, which everybody knows was clownish and vainglorious, but rather his book, stuffed full of so many insults and lies, and restoring the glory and reputation of myself and my associates. God willing, this may still happen.
>
> Indeed, I shall cleanse Rothmann, whether he is still alive or not, from those stains and falsehoods with which he was besmirched by Ursus, upon whom I shall have them pinned to his hurt. I wish you would write this to Rothmann, if he is still alive.[17]

On 26 September 1600 Brahe was not sure whether Rothmann was still alive. A decade earlier, with the Landgrave's permission, Rothmann had visited Uraniburg while he was quite ill.[18] Although expected to return to his astronomical duties in Kassel, instead he went home to his birthplace, Bernburg□ in Anhalt, 79
West Germany. According to an influential historian of astronomy, Rothmann died in 1596.[19] But in 1597 he wrote an (unpublished) theological treatise in Latin (*Restitutio sacramentorum*) and later translated it into German.[20] In 1599 he sent Rollenhagen two letters. Since the later one concerned Ursus, Rollenhagen passed it along to Brahe, who wrote to his former pupil Longberg on 12/22 September 1599:

79. Bernburg, Christopher Rothmann's birthplace, after a drawing by Dilich

> I thought that Rothmann had died. In his recent letter to Rollenhagen, however, I recognized his handwriting and was very happy to learn that he is still alive. Thus that bear and beast from Dithmarschen in his infamous book shamelessly lied twice when he pretends with his very stupid and impertinent mouth that I escaped from Denmark because of some crime that was not trivial and that I had doubtless perpetrated. In like manner he prattles on without any sense that Rothmann was infected and died of I know not what diseases (for it is shameful to mention them), although Rothmann is still alive and in moderately good health. I recently wrote to him and invited him, if his health permitted, [to visit] me[21] [here in Benátky].

But Rothmann's health was so poor that he could not visit Brahe again. Nor is it known exactly when Rothmann died. After his second letter to Rollenhagen in 1599, we hear only that his *Gründlicher, eigentlicher, heller, klarer, kurtzer Bericht von der Tauffe* (Goslar, 1608) was posthumous.[22] The date of Rothmann's birth is likewise unknown. But since he entered the University of Wittenberg on 1 August 1575,[23] and was regarded as precocious, he may have been born around 1560. In his letter to Longberg of 12/22 September 1599, Brahe had an afterthought:

> To add something about that exceedingly wild and ferocious Dithmarschen beast, even though it is not worth mentioning, you should know that several weeks ago, as I recently found out, he fled from Prague. He may have been worried and afraid of just punishment according to law, or planning something secretly in his hideout in his usual way. But in due time he is to be calmly tracked down, brought to justice, and punished, as all good men in Prague recommend. But enough about

> that most insolent pettifogger and falsifier. He will learn the rest from the judge.[24]

With the intention of using Rothmann's 1599 letter in his projected anti-Ursus volume, Brahe made the following request in his letter to Rollenhagen of 26 September 1600:

> If you have any letters written by Rothmann's hand, send them to me enclosed in a letter of your own, in which you testify that the handwriting is his. In this way I may be able to prove that the second letter sent to you toward the end of last year and transmitted to me was written by his hand. When the whole proceeding is finished, and everything is reduced to proper form and printed, I shall see that you get your share. Farewell
> Written in Prague
> 26 September 1600, new style[25]

The proceeding was never finished, and the anti-Ursus volume was never printed because Brahe, the prime mover, died in the midst of his campaign against his adversary. On 20 October 1600 a decision of the Royal Chamber promised Ursus's widow 300 florins for the books seized in compliance with the emperor's order.[26]

XXIX

THE DEATH OF BRAHE

XXIX

THE DEATH OF BRAHE

Brahe's effort to obtain his full measure of revenge on Ursus was thwarted by his unexpected death at a relatively early age. At the end of his collected observations the story of his fatal illness was recorded succinctly by a writer who did not disclose his identity. Hence, when this account was published for the first time, there was no indication who the author was.[1] But his handwriting was later recognized as Kepler's,[2] whose report of Brahe's last days follows. In 1601

> on 13 October Tycho Brahe accompanied [Imperial Councillor Ernfried] Minkawitz to dinner at the home of [Peter Wok Ursinus,] Baron Rosenberg. Holding his urine longer than was his habit, Brahe remained seated. Although he drank a little overgenerously and experienced pressure on his bladder, he felt less concern for the state of his health than for etiquette [which required him not to leave the Baron's dinner table]. By the time Brahe returned home, he could not urinate any more.
>
> At the beginning of this illness the moon was in opposition to Saturn, and a quadrant's distance from Mars, while Mars was in the same place which Tycho had determined as his own ascendant degree.

> He spent five days without sleep. Finally, with the most excruciating pain he barely passed some urine, and yet it was blocked. Uninterrupted insomnia followed; intestinal fever; and little by little, delirium. His poor condition was made worse by his way of eating, from which he could not be deterred. Thus, on 24 October, when his delirium had subsided for a few hours, amid the prayers, tears, and efforts of his family to console him, his strength failed and he passed away very peacefully.
>
> At this time, then, his series of heavenly observations was interrupted, and the observations of thirty-eight years came to an end [Brahe's first recorded observation having been made on 17 August 1563 at the time of a conjunction of Saturn and Jupiter].[3]
>
> During his last night, through the delirium in which everything was very pleasant, like a composer creating a song, Brahe repeated these words over and over again:
>
> Let me not seem to have lived in vain.
>
> Undoubtedly he wanted to add this refrain as a sort of colophon to his works, and by these words dedicate them to the remembrance and advantage of posterity.

Several years later, in Chapter 6 of his *New Astronomy*, Kepler recalled that when Brahe

> lay dying, although he knew that I was of the Copernican persuasion, he asked me to present all my demonstrations in conformity with his hypothesis.[4]

Although Brahe actually died of uremia, his celebrated quarrel with Ursus gave rise to an unfounded rumor. On 22 February/4 March 1602 George Rollenhagen, writing to Kepler from Magdeburg, expressed his conviction that

> in as vigorous a body [as Brahe's] so drastic an effect cannot possibly result from the retention of urine, before a climacteric year.[5]

Rantzau explained that the climacteric years in the life of an individual occurred in two series, multiples of 7 and of 9, with the most critical year being 63, where the two series intersected.[6] Any death happening in a year outside either series was regarded as due to some unnatural cause. Brahe died in the course of his 55th year, between 54 (9 x 6) and 56 (7 x 8). Accordingly Rollenhagen gave credence to the rumor that Brahe had been poisoned by Ursus. Perhaps Rollenhagen did not know that Ursus died on 15 August 1600, over fourteen months before Brahe died on 24 October 1601. Any poison administered by Ursus to Brahe would therefore have been remarkably slow in accomplishing the desired result. Rollenhagen may also have been unaware that after their brief and hostile encounter on Hven in September 1584 Brahe and Ursus never met again. Thereafter, when Brahe wanted to communicate with Ursus, he sent emissaries instead of presenting himself in person.

The depth of Rollenhagen's commitment to astrology is revealed in the postscript of his letter to Kepler, where he wanted to

> know whether at the time of [Brahe's] death the moon was in the last degrees of the Archer, among the malefactors.[7]

By the same token, in a letter to Rantzau, Rollenhagen said:

> I am sending you ... last of all a chart of some plagues in which I wanted to find out whether this evil in some way followed the motion of Saturn.[8]

Rollenhagen's unswerving dependence on omens and portents may be exemplified by his certainty that

As soon as a branch on a certain tree in his garden withered, that signified the impending death of a member of his family.[9]

XXX

KEPLER'S "DEFENSE OF TYCHO AGAINST URSUS"

XXX

KEPLER'S "DEFENSE OF TYCHO AGAINST URSUS"

The Frisian astronomer Fabricius was closely associated with Tycho, both in person and by correspondence. After Brahe's death, Fabricius continued to carry on an extensive correspondence with Kepler, whom he also admired very much. In a letter to Kepler, dated 24 September/3 October 1602, Fabricius remarked:

> I hear that you have also refuted the absurdities of Reimers Ursus's hypotheses. I ask you to publish [your refutation] at the earliest possible time, as you promised Tycho.[1]

Two months later, on 2 December 1602, Kepler replied:

> I have written against Ursus. But I am not satisfied. I must first look at Proclus and Ibn Rushd on the history of hypotheses. I shall publish [this material] some time, when that can be done with less ill-will than now. After all, Ursus was my predecessor [as Imperial Mathematician].[2]

As things turned out, Kepler never found the time to do the research he planned on the *Summary of the Hypotheses of the Astronomers* by Proclus (410-485), the famous head of the Platonic Academy in Athens. Lack of time also prevented Kepler from delving into the discussions of astronomical hypotheses in the commentaries of Ibn Rushd (Averroes, 1126-1198) on Aristotle, As a result, Kepler never overcame his dissatisfaction with what he had written against Ursus. Hence he left his marvelous *Defense of Tycho against Ursus* in an unfinished state.

The incomplete manuscript suffered the same fate as the rest of Kepler's unpublished remains, buffeted hither and thither by the shifting fortunes of the Thirty Years War and the faltering treasuries of the various governments defaulting on their obligations to his heirs. From his son's heirs, the renowned astronomer Johannes Hevelius (1611-1687) bought their holdings. Compiling the first catalog of the Kepler manuscripts, he published it in the Royal Society of London's *Philosophical Transactions,* with his twenty-ninth and last fascicle containing Kepler's "Tractate against Ursus."[3]
A century later, in 1773, on the recommendation of the
eminent mathematician Leonhard Euler□ (1707-1783), 80
Czarina Catherine II□ purchased the Kepler manu- 81
scripts. Through the good offices of the Russian ambassador to the Duchy of Württemberg, several volumes were sent to the duchy's capital, Stuttgart, for the use of Christian Frisch (1807-1882), the editor of the eight volumes of the first and still the only complete edition of Kepler's works. In Frisch's first volume Kepler's *Defense of Tycho Brahe against Ursus* was published for the first time (F *1*: 236-276).

If a writer wanted to attach a date to something he had written, he often did so at the end. The *Defense,* which Kepler abandoned shortly before reaching its end, carries no formal date. However, the preface begins by recalling that Ursus "published ... a little book *On Astronomical Hypotheses* three years ago." Since Ursus's title page bore the date "In the year 1597," Kepler wrote the preface in 1600. It also recalled that "Nicholas Ursus was the mathematician of His

80. Leonhard Euler (1707-1783), portrait painted in Berlin, 1753, by Emanuel Handmann (1718-1781), and preserved in the Aula of the Basel Museum, Switzerland; engraving by Friedrich Weber (1813-1882) in 1851

81. Catherine II, czarina of Russia from 1762 to 1796, portrait painted about 1760 by Count Pietro Antonio Rotari of Verona (1707-1762), and preserved in the Russian Museum, Leningrad

Imperial Majesty during his lifetime." Since Ursus died on 15 August 1600, Kepler began the preface in 1600, after 15 August. Hence we must correct Frisch's statement (F *1*: 235/13↑) that Kepler undertook the task of writing against Ursus "at the beginning of the year 1601." Moreover, Frisch placed Kepler at that time in Graz. But he was in Prague, not Graz, then. He himself says that he left Graz in 1600 "on 30 September, beginning my journey to Prague."[4] In 1601, "leaving my wife behind in Prague, from April to the end of August I went on a trip to Styria,"[5] of which Graz was the capital. Hence "at the beginning of the year 1601," before April, Kepler was not in Graz. He recalled that "from October 1600 to August 1601 a fever gripped me. In the meantime I wrote against Ursus on Tycho's orders."[6] Kepler himself tells us, then, that he wrote the *Defense* in Prague, beginning in October 1600, while he was suffering from a persistent fever. On 8 February 1601 he informed Maestlin, as we have already seen,[7] that

> on account of this illness of mine I am doing nothing but writing against Ursus.[8]

In April 1601 Kepler left Prague for Graz in a fruitless[9] effort of four or five months to salvage his wife's Styrian holdings. Returning to Prague,

> from September, I say, I began to investigate with the utmost care the amount of the sun's second eccentricity, the task in which Tycho [was engaged when he] died [on 24 October]. We spent a month taking care of him while he was sick and in burying him after his death.[10]

In 1601, from April through August while Kepler was in Styria looking after his wife's property, he did not write any part of the *Defense*. Nor did he resume work on the *Defense* after he returned to Prague in September, when he began to undertake a technical astronomical investigation with Brahe. Since Tycho did not insist on his continuing the *Defense*, it languished where Kepler had dropped it when he left for Graz in April. Accordingly, Kepler wrote his unfinished *Defense of Tycho Brahe against Ursus* in Prague in about half a year, from October 1600 to April 1601

The *Defense's* preface reported that Ursus's *Astro-* 82
nomical Hypotheses □

> narrated the history of the hypotheses and finally reached my very good friend Helisaeus Roeslin, M.D. For the purpose of refuting Roeslin's opinion, Ursus adduced a certain theorem [4, Book VI] of Euclid, and based his reasoning on the data needed to measure the sizes of the planetary spheres by a geometrical method (a procedure familiar to astronomers). Ursus added that on the same basis it was possible to analyze the propositions published by me in the preceding year under the title *Cosmographic Mystery*.
>
> Seizing that opportunity, he inserted in his little book a letter [dated 15 November 1595] in which I had consulted him about my discovery two years before. He earned my most uncivil thanks. I wrote as a young man, twenty-three years old, with very little sincerity, of course. For I went far out of bounds in two respects: in praising Ursus, and in subordinating myself to him. With complete confidence in the outcome, I looked forward at least to receiving an answer. Ursus's character was reputed to be such that these weapons [flattery and subservience] were necessary to overcome his silence. But if anybody does not understand my intention, he will rightly be angry at me for harming many top mathematicians in Europe by my extravagant praise of Ursus. Those who know me well will even be amazed at my honoring Ursus as my teacher instead of Maestlin,

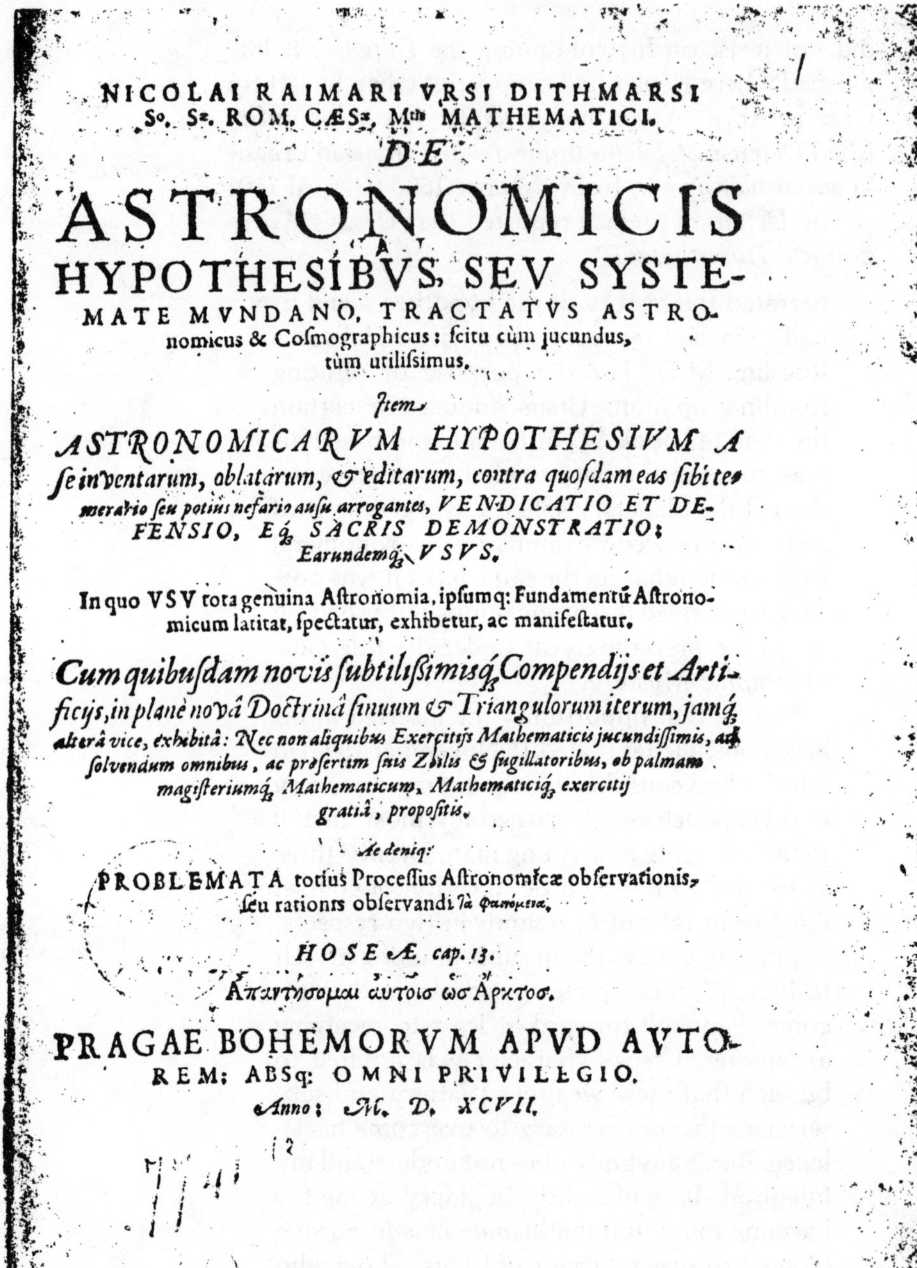

NICOLAI RAIMARI VRSI DITHMARSI
So. Sæ. ROM. CÆSæ. Mtis MATHEMATICI.
DE
ASTRONOMICIS
HYPOTHESIBVS, SEV SYSTEMATE MVNDANO, TRACTATVS ASTRONOMICUS & Cosmographicus: scitu cùm jucundus, tùm utilissimus.

Item

ASTRONOMICARVM HYPOTHESIVM A se inventarum, oblatarum, & editarum, contra quosdam eas sibi temerario seu potius nefario ausu arrogantes, VENDICATIO ET DEFENSIO, Eq; SACRIS DEMONSTRATIO: Earundemq; VSVS.

In quo VSV tota genuina Astronomia, ipsumq; Fundamentũ Astronomicum latitat, spectatur, exhibetur, ac manifestatur.

Cum quibusdam novis subtilissimisq; Compendijs et Artificijs, in planè novâ Doctrinâ sinuum & Triangulorum iterum, jamq; alterâ vice, exhibitâ: Nec non aliquibus Exercitijs Mathematicis jucundissimis, ad solvendum omnibus, ac præsertim suis Zoilis & sugillatoribus, ob palmam magisteriumq; Mathematicum, Mathematiciq; exercitij gratiâ, propositis.

Ac deniq;

PROBLEMATA totius Processus Astronomicæ observationis, seu rationis observandi τὰ φαινόμενα.

HOSEÆ cap. 13.

Ἀπαντήσομαι αὐτοῖς ὡς Ἄρκτος.

PRAGAE BOHEMORVM APVD AVTOREM: ABSq; OMNI PRIVILEGIO.

Anno: M. D. XCVII.

82. Title Page of Nicholas Reimers Ursus's *Astronomical Hypotheses,* Prague, 1597

and ascribing to Ursus the little I know about mathematics. Yet I had never seen Ursus, I had never heard him speak, except in his *Foundation of Astronomy*. What I have said thus far, however, may seem trivial. What follows is more serious. For Ursus wants to appear to be honoring me by printing my letter when he pronounces it worth publishing. Yet he did not leave in the dark what he was looking for.

In the first place, in the title of his little book, from the noble and illustrious lord, Tycho Brahe of Denmark, Lord of Knudstrup and Uraniburg etc., he snatches the invention of the new hypotheses and claims it for himself.

The title page of his book boldly proclaimed:

Nicholas Reimers Ursus of Dithmarschen,
Mathematician of His Majesty, the Holy Roman Emperor
Astronomical and Cosmographical Treatise on Astronomical Hypotheses,
or on the System of the Universe, a Treatise that Is Pleasant and Also Very Useful to Know
In Addition, a Validation and Defense of the Astronomical Hypotheses Invented, Propounded, and Published by Himself,
against Certain Persons who Dare to Claim These Hypotheses
for themselves Imprudently or rather Criminally

Among these imprudent or criminal claimants was Brahe. Ursus's title page advertised:

Also a Demonstration of these Hypotheses on the Basis of Holy Scripture, and their Use. All the Real Astronomy and its Astronomical Foundation Lie Hidden in this Use, Are Examined, Brought to Light, and Made Clear.
With Certain Novel and Very Subtle Summaries and Devices,
in an Entirely New Theory of Sines and Triangles, Explained Again, Now for the Second Time.

(the first time had been Ursus's *Foundation of Astronomy* (Strasbourg, 1588). In the *Defense's* preface Kepler's analysis of Ursus's strategy proceeded as follows:

> My letter contained these words: "I love your hypotheses" [sig. D1r]. By means of my letter, Ursus thought, he was going to prove there are men who recognize the justice of his case. In this way he involved me in a dispute not my own, and extorted evidence from someone who did not know [what was going on].
>
> Secondly, toward the bottom of his title page Ursus announces his erudition in this little book, as though for the Olympic games, and challenges all comers, obviously including Tycho Brahe, for the gold medal and championship in mathematics.

Ursus's title page also

> Propounded to Everybody, Particularly His Detractors and Vilifiers, Some Very Delightful Mathematical Problems to be Solved for the Prize and Mathematical Championship, and for Practice in Mathematics
> Finally, Problems Involving the Whole Process of Astronomical Observation or the Method of Observing the Phenomena

In the same spirit, while Ursus was working as a surveyor, he had proposed that nobody should be permitted to practice surveying in Denmark and Schleswig-Holstein before solving the problem propounded in his *Geodaesia Ranzoviana* at sig. L3r-v. He set the tone of his *Astronomical Hypotheses* by a pugnacious quotation from the Septuagint (Hosea 13:8):

> I will meet them as a bear [that is bereaved of her whelps]

In his *Defense*'s preface Kepler resumed his analysis of Ursus's strategy with a light touch of irony:

> Very obligingly, he inserts my letter in his little book as if it took the place of a judge handing down the decision that Ursus indisputably deserves the gold medal.
>
> Lastly, in that letter I had mentioned Tycho in very honorific terms, and I had asked Ursus to

> pass on this discovery of mine to him in Denmark. For being on very friendly terms with his enemy Tycho, Ursus decided to punish me. His method was none other than to erase the reference to Tycho in my letter, which he inserted in his little book, written and published for no other purpose than to destroy Tycho's reputation.

According to the preface, Kepler's letter to Ursus of 15 November 1595 referred to Brahe, that reference being later erased by Ursus when he inserted the letter in his *Astronomical Hypotheses*. The original of Kepler's letter is lost, together with the rest of Ursus's papers. Kepler made and kept no copy of the letter.[11] Hence, the only surviving version of the letter is what Ursus printed. What he printed does not mention Brahe, for the simple reason that Brahe was not mentioned in Kepler's first letter to Ursus. Kepler did mention Brahe in his second letter to Ursus, written in October 1597. But Ursus did not publish that letter, which was written and received after the *Astronomical Hypotheses* had been printed in the spring of 1597. The letter from Kepler which Ursus did publish contained no reference to Brahe when Ursus received it. Ursus must therefore be cleared of the charge that he deleted a reference to Brahe. Kepler's accusation was undoubtedly advanced in good faith, but he relied on his imperfect recollection, conflating his second letter to Ursus with his first.[12] Unaware of the falsity of the accusation in his preface, Kepler continued:

> As a result I, who had praised Tycho to Ursus privately, was punished by being compelled to praise Tycho's assailant to everybody publicly. Since Ursus chose to abuse my letter in so many ways, it is now obvious why he deemed it worth publishing. For as far as my discovery is concerned, if that deserves publication, by Ursus's own admission he had already seen it,

> since the entire book [Kepler's *Cosmographic Mystery*] was commercially available, and there was no need for Ursus's publication of the letter. How much this publication bothered me, I testified in letters to Tycho[13] and Roeslin.

Brahe was not the only target of Ursus's ferocious attacks in his *Astronomical Hypotheses.* Roeslin was assailed even more viciously. But in the *Defense* Kepler confined his counterpunches to the protection of Brahe. He completely ignored Ursus's blows aimed at Roeslin. Clearly, then, Kepler intended this *Defense* to be essentially a reply to Ursus on behalf of Brahe, and not a general counteroffensive against Ursus. Kepler took up the cudgels against one Imperial Mathematician in favor of his successor. While Kepler was writing the *Defense* he could not foresee that just as Brahe succeeded Ursus as Imperial Mathematician, so he, Kepler, would in turn succeed Brahe. While Kepler's letter to Brahe of 19 February 1599 has survived, his letter to Roeslin is lost. A dozen years later, however, Roeslin referred to it in his *Discourse* (Strasbourg, 1609):

> In a letter from Styria, Kepler urged Roeslin to respond to Reimers Ursus, the Imperial Mathematician at that time, in the matter of his little book against Tycho Brahe and Roeslin. But Roeslin did not regard Ursus as worth answering. Soon thereafter Ursus was rewarded by a timely death, and in his place (to the especially great delight of Roeslin) Kepler became the Imperial Mathematician. Roeslin deemed Kepler worthy of replying to Ursus.[14]

To this, Kepler responded in his *Answer to Roeslin's*
83 *Discourse*□ (Prague, 1609):

> I do not recall the content of my letter very well after so many years. Still, I can imagine what impelled me to write it. Ursus had my private letter to himself printed, and he did so in a book aimed at my good friends, Tycho Brahe and Roeslin. That grieved me.[15]

Antwort

Joannis Keppleri S. C. M^tis: Mathematici

Auff

D. Heliſæi Röslini Medici & Philoſophi Diſcurs

Von heutiger zeit beſchaffenheit/ vnd wie es ins künfftig ergehen werde.

Belangend ſonderlich etliche puncten/ ſo D. Röslin auß *Kepleri* Buch *de Stellâ Anni 1604.* angezogen.

Allen Liebhabern der wahren Philoſophia, ſonderlich aber auch denen/ wölche künfftige Sachen gern wiſſen wolten zu ſonderm Nutz vnd vnderricht/ warauff ſie ſich entlich zuverlaſſen haben.

Gedruckt zu Prag bey Pauln Seſſe

Im Jahr/ 1609.

83. Title Page of Kepler's *Reply to Roeslin*, Prague, 1609

Kepler expressed his grief not only in letters to Brahe and Roeslin but also by word of mouth to Ursus, as he reported in the *Defense's* preface:

> Moreover, last January, as soon as I arrived in Prague, I told Ursus to his face [how much his publication bothered me]. But I concealed my name lest he intensify the situation to a brawl if he knew he was dealing with Kepler in person. I also added that since he decided to drag me, who had written as a pupil, unwillingly to the judge's seat, he should therefore permit me to discard a pupil's modesty and to assume a judge's authority in that literary contest (for I was leaving to Tycho the proceedings concerned with his crimes and civil torts) and in my turn to decide publicly what seems to be the mathematical issue. In this way I finally revealed my name and left him peacefully.
>
> Although I indicated to Ursus that I would refute his publication, I was prevented from putting my hand to that project later on by many obligations, mainly connected with my household. Moreover, Ursus died in the meantime [on 15 August 1600]. This raised some doubt in my mind whether there would not be those who would deprecate this struggle with a dead man. Yet I had in the first instance volunteered to transfer this task to myself from the shoulders of Tycho Brahe, who was insisting upon my promise. It was, moreover, in itself an honorable mission to uproot mistaken beliefs in students' minds, and to counteract the downgrading of mathematical discoveries that has been implanted in the minds of [potential] patrons. It is also not unusual for survivors to evaluate the opinions and publications of those who have died, whatever their merits (Ursus himself approves of this practice by
> 84 censuring Ramus [Pierre de la Ramée]□ after

his death [in 1572], on page 2 of signature C [of the *Astronomical Hypotheses*]).

84. Pierre de la Ramée (Peter Ramus, 1515-1572), royal lecturer in France

Without mentioning La Ramée by name, Ursus vigorously rejected his idea that astronomy had once had no hypotheses and did not need any. In the margin of sig. C1v Ursus bluntly asserted: "Hypotheses are necessary." His accompanying text declared:

> For it is obvious that without the assistance and aid of these fictitious suppositions or hypotheses, the motions of the heavenly bodies, the phenomena of the heavenly motions and, finally, their computation cannot in any way be preserved and performed. Yet certain people ignorantly make the opposite statement and declaration, with dreams and pretenses about some old astronomy of the ancient Babylonians and Egyptians. Hence, opposition and laughter should be the response to the witlessness and insanity of certain people who foolishly deny the need for hypotheses. They rashly maintain that astronomy can be completely established; constructed, and perfected without hypotheses and by logical reasoning alone (if they can do so, why then don't they, I ask), as if logic by itself were enough to reach all goals and did not require the other specialized disciplines.

Then, in the margin of sig. C2r, Ursus insisted: "Astronomy was never without hypotheses." In the accompanying text he said:

> I confess that I cannot be persuaded by any arguments that astronomy was cultivated and maintained, that the computation of the heavenly motions was properly performed, without hypotheses. For what sort of astronomy will there be, I ask, when it is deprived of its twin Platonic wings (I mean, arithmetic and geometry), and they have been cut off or thrown away? Surely [astronomy will be] crippled, mutilated, and absolutely incomplete. For in the computation of the heavenly motions, the periodic time must be known, and therefore the periods themselves. But these periods are most conveniently predicted and conceived by means of imaginary circles.

> Lastly, those circles and the mechanical delineation of them, constitute and create the hypotheses. Now that cycle of the necessity of hypotheses is visible and apparent. Those hypotheses, therefore, are so necessary that without them nothing certain or true can be determined and accomplished in the computation and observation of the motions of the heavenly bodies. It stands to reason, accordingly, that the method of hypotheses was known even to the earliest astronomers and is much older than is commonly said.

Following Ursus's example in replying to La Ramée after his death, Kepler ended the *Defense's* preface by answering Ursus after his death:

> Therefore, after thinking it over for a long time, I finally undertook this little essay in a sincere spirit and with a zeal for mathematics. I have composed it in such a way, I believe, that there will accrue to me, praise for defending the truth, and to the reader, benefit in perceiving it.

To eradicate mistaken beliefs; to persuade those who are in a position, whether by virtue of private wealth or political power, to support genuine research, vilified by the jealous or by the incompetent; and to disseminate the truth—these are the noble purposes, far transcending the personal motives, for which Kepler wrote his *Defense of Tycho against Ursus*. When he started it, he fully intended to finish it, as is shown by his choice of the word *pertexuisse*, which means "to continue a weaving operation right through to the end." But the weaving of the seamless robe of the *Defense* was interrupted just short of the end.

NOTES

NOTES ON CHAPTER I

Brahe's Publication of His Hypothesis

1. TB *8*:47/11-13; GW *13*:200/125-128; F *1*:219/9↑-7↑. The time when Brahe wrote Chapter VIII of *Stella caudata*, as published, was grossly misunderstood by Pierre Duhem (1861-1916). In his famous essay "Sozein ta phainomena" (*Annales de philosophie chrétienne, 1908, 156*:566; reprinted in book form, Paris: Vrin, 1983), Duhem stated: "c'est en 1578 que Tycho Brahé rédigea les huit premiers chapitres de son ouvrage sur la comète de 1577." This serious blunder was made even worse by the English mistranslation: "the first eight chapters were completed by 1578"; P. Duhem, *To Save the Phenomena*, tr. E. Doland and C. Maschler (University of Chicago Press, 1969), p. 96.

2. A heroic poem in Latin verse about the *History of the Ditmarschen War, Waged in 1559*, completed by the poet laureate Hieronymus (H)Osius on 1 January 1560, was published in Simon Schard, *Rerum germanicarum scriptores varii*, ed. Hieronymus Thomae (Giessen, 1673), III, 46-65. For recent views of the Ditmarschen War, see Nis Rudolf Nissen in Alfred Kamphausen, N.R. Nissen, and Erich Wohlenberg, *Ditmarschen: Geschichte und Bild einer Landschaft* (Heide in Holstein, 1968), pp. 61-62, and Gottfried Ernst Hoffman, in *Geschichte Schleswig-Holsteins* (begun by Volquart Pauls), V, 1 (Neumünster, 1972), pp. 17-26. Under his own name Rantzau wrote about the preservation of health (Leipzig, 1576; 5 editions in all); interpretation of dreams (Rostock, 1591);

patrons of astrology (Antwerp, 1580; Leipzig, 1581, 1584, 1585); *Horoscopographia* (Strasbourg, 1585; Wittenberg, 1588; Schleswig, 1591); *Ranzovianum calendarium* (Hamburg, 1590; Leipzig, 1592); *Diarium* (Wittenberg, 1593, 1598; Hamburg, 1594, 1596; Leipzig, 1596); *Tractatus astrologicus* (Frankfurt, 1593, 1600, 1602, 1615, 1625, 1633; Wittenberg, 1594; Hamburg, 1594). *Directiones* was a posthumous work (Frankfurt, 1611, 1624, 1627). Brahe's *Astronomiae instauratae mechanica* (Wandsbek, 1598) was printed on his own press while he was a guest in a castle owned by Rantzau, who helped to obtain Brahe's appointment as Imperial Mathematician of the Holy Roman Empire after Brahe had left Denmark. A useful lecture on Rantzau was published by P. Hasse in *Zeitschrift der Gesellschaft für Schleswig-Holstein-Lauenburgische Geschichte*, 1878, *8*:329-348; for additional discussion of Rantzau in this periodical, see the Index to volumes 1-20 (Kiel, 1899), p. 157/left/9-7↑; Index to volumes 21-30 (Kiel, 1904), p. 152/left/2-14; and the Index to volumes 51-60 (Neumünster, 1938), p. 182/left/3↑-right/8.

3. TB 7:127/9-10.

4. *De mundi aetherei recentioribus phaenomenis liber secundus qui est de illustri stella caudata* (Uraniburg, 1588), VIII; TB 4:156/34-157/41, with diagram at 4:158; summary and diagram in Dreyer, pp. 167-169; diagram in *Vistas in Astronomy*, 1975, *17*:xxxiii, fig. 25; partial translation in Marie Boas (Hall) and A. Rupert Hall, "Tycho Brahe's System of the World," *Occasional Notes of the Royal Astronomical Society*, 1959, *3*:257-263.

5. TB 7:131/14-20.

6. TB 7:135/38-42.

7. TB 7:125/20-22. Rollenhagen became better known for his satirical poem *Froschmeuseler* (Battle of the Frogs and Mice), which he dedicated to Rantzau on 21 March 1595 (ed. Magdeburg, 1608, sig. A 2v-3v, 3v-6v).

8. Ursus, *Fundamentum astronomicum* (Strasbourg, 1588; cited hereafter as UFA), fol. 41: Diagram of the System of Nature, representing the hypotheses of the motions of the heavenly bodies.

NOTES ON CHAPTER II

Brahe's Discovery of Ursus's Plagiarism

1. TB 7:148/22-28.
2. TB 7:148/33-35.
3. TB 7:149/8-30.
4. NCCW, I, fol. 9r/17↑-16↑: *circa ipsum esse centrum mundi*; fol. 10r/2: *In medio ... omnium residet.*
5. TB 7:149/30-41.
6. TB 7:167/1-7.
7. TB 7:387/16-19.
8. TB *6*:179/20-23.
9. TB 7:387/19-23.
10. See Ch. i at n. 6.
11. TB 7:387/23-38.
12. TB 7:126/5-9; 127/26-131/8.
13. TB 7:387/38-388/21.
14. TB 7:388/21-389/31.

NOTES ON CHAPTER III

The Landgrave's Planetarium

1. Johann Ephraim Scheibel, *Einleitung zur mathematischen Bücherkenntnis* (1784-1789, Breslau), III, 15th-16th Stück, p. 154.
2. TB *6*:134/13-15.
3. TB *6*:147/1-12.
4. TB *6*:156/38-40; 157/8-10, 16-17.
5. TB *6*:179/14-25; F *1*:226/27-35.
6. F *1*:226/36-5↑.
7. TB *6*:179/26-180/14.

NOTES ON CHAPTER IV

Ursus in Strasbourg

1. UFA, sig.*2r-v.
2. F *1*:229/14↑-4↑.
3. F *1*:229/3↑-230/6.
4. *Epistolae ad J. Kepplerum*, ed. Michael Gottlieb Hansch (Leipzig, 1718), p. 90/n. 1/2↑: "in Hassia delineatum 1586"; GW *13*:390 on 69/10; F *1*:227/#1/6.
5. F *1*:230/7-15.
6. Roeslin's kinsman has not yet been identified.
7. F *1*:229/30-15↑.
8. F *1*:228/13↑-11↑.
9. This scholar has not yet been identified.
10. Although Roeslin was a reasonably well-informed man, he was not aware that Brahe had been appointed Ursus's successor as Imperial Mathematician, a post not expressly created for Brahe (as in GW *19*:7*/12↑-11↑). Brahe was appointed shortly before 1/10 December 1599, his salary to be paid retroactively from 1 May 1599. After he complained about nonpayment, on 13 July 1600 he received 2000 gulden as his annual stipend (TB *8*:168/#173, 208/#201). Two days after Brahe's death on 24 October 1601 Kepler was appointed his successor.
11. This correspondence was initiated by Kepler, who had become feverishly ill when he took part in a student play out of doors in February 1591. Half a year later, after receiving the Master of Arts degree, he suffered a relapse. According to his astrological calculations, this illness should not occur during the twenty-first year. Hence he consulted the famous physician-astrologer Roeslin who, convinced that such maladies are not restricted to particular years, sent Kepler his horoscope on 17 October 1592 (GW *19*:320-321). In F *8*:294-295, "1593" is either a misreading or a misprint, repeated by Paul Diesner, "Der elsässiche Arzt Dr. Helisaeus Röslin als Forscher und Publizist," Elsass-Lothringische Wissenschaftliche Gesellschaft zu Strassburg, *Jahrbuch*, 1935, *11*:213/#4/2.

12. F *1*:228/10 -229/26. Roeslin discussed the 1604 nova's astrological significance in his *Judicium* (Strasbourg, 1605; reprinted in GW *1*:483-485). This *Judicium* was also issued as an addition to an unauthorized reprint of Kepler's *Gründtlicher Bericht* (Prague, 1605; reprinted in F *1*: 473-478, and GW *1*:391-399). In his *New Star* of 1606 Kepler commented unfavorably on the *Judicium* of Roeslin, who replied in his *Discurs*, which he dedicated on 26 June 1609. On 8 September 1609 Kepler dedicated his *Antwort ... auff... Roeslini ... Discurs* (Reply to Roeslin's *Discurs*; reprinted in GW *4*:99-144).

13. F *1*:228/36-48.

14. GW *13*:390 on #69, last 4 lines.

15. The original letter is preserved in the library of the University of Munich, Cod. 692, pp. 438-461. It was published in part in GW *13*: #68.

16. Cope († c. 1580), a Catholic who left England for religious reasons, "was author or publisher of some pieces much esteemed among the learned," according to *The Church History of England from the Year 1500, to the Year 1688* (Brussels, 1737-1742), II, 62. This three-volume work, published anonymously, is attributed to Charles Dodd, a pseudonym of Hugh Tootell. Whether these learned pieces included a "Chronotheatrum," which Ursus's Prague opponents accused him of plagiarizing, has not been determined.

17. UAH, sig. H2v/9↑-3↑.

NOTES ON CHAPTER V

Ursus's Appointment as Imperial Mathematician

1. Jacob Grimm, *Deutsches Wörterbuch*, I (Leipzig, 1854), xx/7↑-5↑.

2. J.G.L. Blumhof, *Vom alten Mathematiker Conrad Dasypodius* (Göttingen, 1796), p. 16n.

3. Adam Gauthier Strobel, *Histoire du Gymnase protestant de Strasbourg* (Strasbourg, 1838), p. 119/17, p. 153/2; DSB, III, 585.

4. *Jean Sturm*: *Classicae epistolae* (Paris/Strasbourg, 1938), p. 3, n. 4, p. 90, n. 2, ed. Jean Rott.
5. J.H. Zedler, *Universal Lexicon*, VII (Halle/Leipzig, 1734), 225; C.G. Jöcher, *Allgemeines Gelehrten-Lexicon*, II (Leipzig, 1750), 37; A.G. Kästner, *Geschichte der Mathematik*, I (Göttingen, 1796; reprint, Hildesheim, 1970), 340.
6. GW *14*:#152/7-8.
7. Rott (p.3, n.4): 20 April; Melchior Adam, *Vitae Germanorum philosophorum* (Heidelberg, 1615), p. 441,p. 442/19↑-17↑: 22 April; Jöcher, and *Allgemeine deutsche Biographie*, IV (Leipzig, 1876; reprint, Berlin, 1968), 764/2: 26 April.
8. Henning Witte, *Diarium biographicum* (Danzig, 1688) and J.F. Weidler, *Historia astronomiae* (Wittenberg, 1741), p. 381/11-12: 20 April 1601.
9. GW *15*: 388/91.
10. GW *15*: #283/61-65, pp. 502-503.
11. GW *15*: #283/65-107.
12. UFA, sig. *4r/8-9, fol. 9r. For Bürgi's work at Kassel, see Ludolf v. Mackensen, *Die erste Sternwarte Europas* (Munich, 1979), pp. 21-60.
13. UFA, fol. 9v/14-24, fol. 10r.
14. UFA, sig. *2v/20-21, fol. 11r.
15. UFA, fol. 12v.
16. UFA, fol. 16v.
17. UFA, fol. 17r.
18. UFA, fol. 17v.
19. UFA, fol. 21r.
20. UFA, fol. 21v.
21. UFA, fol. 22r.
22. UFA, fol. 23v.
23. UFA, fol. 25r.
24. UFA, fol. 26r.
25. UFA, fol. 29r.
26. C.J. Gerhardt, *Geschichte der Mathematik in Deutschland* (Munich, 1877; reprint, New York/London,

1965), pp. 84-87; Peter Treutlein, "Die deutsche Coss," *Zeitschrift für Mathematik und Physik*, 1879, 24, Supplement, pp. 99-101.

27. UFA, fol. 35r. Schönfeld died on 13 June 1591, according to Freher (p. 1293), relying on Marburg documents.

28. UFA, fol. 36r.

29. UFA, fol. 40v; *The Mathematicall Praeface to the Elements of Geometrie of Euclid of Megara* (1570), introduction by Allen G. Debus (New York, 1975).

30. UFA, sig. K6.

31. UFA, sig. *2v/17-19, fol. 6v.

32. TB 7: 305/8-12.

NOTES ON CHAPTER VI

The Kepler-Ursus Correspondence

1. GW *13*:48/1-14; F *1*:218/23↑-12↑.

2. Because he omitted the last four lines, in his letter to Ursus Kepler had to modify the sixth line. In the ninth line, the misprint *nominis* is repeated in GW *1*:4, although the correct reading *mominis* = *moviminis* had been explained in F *1*:193/n. 26.

3. GW *13*:49/35-38; F *1*:219/3-6.

4. This letter was misdated in 1596 by Max Brod, *The Redemption of Tycho Brahe* (New York, 1928; translation of Brod's *Tycho Brahes Weg zu Gott*), pp. 131-132; Edward Rosen, "Brod's Brahe: Fact vs. Fiction," *Sudhoffs Archiv*, 1982, *66*:70-78.

5. Edward Rosen, "Kepler's Defense of Tycho against Ursus," *Popular Astronomy*, 1946, *54*:410/n. 5.

6. *Catalogus novus nundinarum vernalium, Francofurti ad Moenum*, anno MDXCVII (Frankfurt, 1597), sig. D3r/10 -7 .

7. GW *13*:124/6-8; F *1*:219/11-13.

8. Hansch, p. 90; F *1*:277/n. 1; GW *13*:390 on #69.

9. Bürgi (1552-1632) was born in Lichtensteig on the banks of the River Thur in Switzerland, not in the principality of Liechtenstein on the banks of the River Rhein (as in DSB, *2*: 602).

10. *Prodromus dissertationum cosmographicarum continens mysterium cosmographicum* ... (Forerunner of Cosmographical Dissertations, Containing the Cosmographical Mystery ...), translated as Johannes Kepler, *The Secret of the Universe*, by A.M. Duncan, with an introduction and commentary by E.J. Aiton, and a preface by I. Bernard Cohen (New York: Abaris, 1981). Brod referred to "the modestly entitled *Prodromus*" (p. 3). Yet as the forerunner of such cosmographical dissertations as Kepler's *New Astronomy* and his *Harmonics of the Universe*, it claimed it contained the cosmographical mystery, that is, the secret key to the structure of the cosmos, hardly a modest title.

11. GW *13*:124/14-125/32; F *1*:219/17-31.

12. GW *13*:125/36-37.

13. Brod's Kepler (p. 92/7↑-4↑) says he "had nothing to do with" the *Cosmographic Mystery*: "Friends put it together for me out of papers scattered all over the place and sent it to the printer." Actually, Kepler's labors on the *Cosmographic Mystery* were intense, and his only helper was Maestlin, who saw it through the press for him in Tübingen, while he himself was in Graz.

14. GW *13*:143/126-129; F *1*:36/2↑-37/1.

15. GW *13*:143/129-130; F *1*:37/1-2.

16. GW *13*:261/480-481; F *1*:233/13↑-12↑.

17. GW *13*:261/476-480; F *1*:233/18↑-14↑.

18. GW *13*:261/482-483; F *1*:233/11↑.

19. GW *13*:261/484-487; F *1*:233/10↑-7↑.

NOTES ON CHAPTER VII

Kepler and Herwart

1. Grienberger later moved to Rome, where he succeeded Christopher Clavius as the teacher of mathematics in the Collegio Romano. For Grienberger's publications, see C. Sommervogel, ed., *Bibliothèque de la Compagnie de Jésus, 3* (Brussels/Paris, 1892), col. 1810-1812.

2. Having no access to the original, and relying instead on a book printed in 1796, F *1*:60/21↑, 3↑, misdated this letter 17 September. The correct date, 12 September, is based on Kepler's fair copy and Herwart's answer (GW *13*:132/26, 147/2).

3. The conflict (and intermarriage) between the Protestant Keplerian and Catholic Ficklerian branches of the family were discussed in Gruner, pp. 30-33.

4. GW *13*:132/22-24; F *1*:60/25↑-23↑.

5. GW *13*:393/5↑-3↑.

6. GW *13*:147/1-3; F *1*:60/6↑-2↑.

7. GW *13*:150.

8. Sebald Kepler, the Jesuit, was born on 13 November 1552 (Gruner, pp. 197, 199/ #24). In later letters to Herwart (24 December 1597, 16 December 1598) Kepler explained that his studies gave him no time to write to Fickler, to whom he asked to be remembered. Fickler was admitted to the University of Ingolstadt on 5 August 1551; see *Die Matrikel der Ludwig--Maximilians-Universität Ingolstadt-Landshut-München*, I (Munich, 1937), 679. After receiving the M.A. degree there in 1555, ten years later he obtained a doctorate in both civil and canon law from the University of Bologna. In an official capacity in 1562-1564 he attended the Council of Trent, of which his *Historical Description* occupies Vol. VII, part 2, pages 255-400, in Jodocus LePlat, *Monumentorum ad historiam Concilii Tridentini ... collectio* (Louvain, 1781-1787). After *De iure magistratuum in subditos, et officio subditorum erga magistratus* had been published anonymously in 1576, this Calvinist work *On the Rights of Rulers over their Subjects and the Duty of Subjects toward their Rulers* was answered by Fickler, using exactly the same Latin title (Ingolstadt, 1578). These are only two of his approximately twenty publications, to say nothing about his numerous unpublished writings left in manuscript.

9. GW *13*:177.

10. GW *13*:205-206, 217; F *1*:66-67. Praetorius's April letter is crudely mistranslated by Robert S. Westman, p. 303, *The Copernican Achievement* (Berkeley/-London, 1975), reviewed in the *Polish Review*, 1976, *21*:225-235.

11. GW *13*:155-160; F *1*:61.

12. GW *13*:178/17-20; F *1*:61/last 3 lines. Since Lansberge's astronomical works had not yet been printed, Herwart's misconception of his Copernican ideas was based on hearsay and correspondence (not with Lansberge).

13. *Triangulorum geometriae libri IV* (Leiden, 1591).

14. In his letters to Kepler of 10 March and 12 March 1598, Herwart had raised the question of the compass; GW *13*:177-178.

15. In his letter of 15 November 1595, Kepler did not call Ursus "Reinmarus," nor did he see that distortion of the author's name in the copy of the *Chronotheatrum* which Raimarus Ursus forwarded together with his letter of 29 May 1597 to Kepler.

16. GW *13*:193/174-178, 199-203; F *1*:64/18↑-14↑, 65/7-8; F *2*:813/8-10.

17. GW *13*:179/10, 15; 229/401; F *2*:16/13↑-4↑; 23/33-34.

18. Magini, *Novae coelestium orbium theoricae congruentes cum observationibus N. Copernici*, preface, sig. c6v/5-16; address to the reader, sig. b4r/last line-b4v/6.

19. TB *5*:126/11-12; *7*:317/9-10; Antonio Favaro, *Carteggio inedito di Ticone Brahe ... con G. A. Magini* (Bologna, 1886), p. 393/15↑-14↑. Magini's letter was published in *Astronomiae instauratae mechanica*, which Brahe dedicated to Rudolph II on New Year's Eve, 1598, so that some word about Magini's brief and general approval of Brahe's cosmology may have reached Kepler by 26 March 1598, when he wrote this letter to Herwart.

20. GW *13*:193/178-180; F *1*:64/14↑-12↑.

21. Roeslin, *Work of God the Creator*, p. 21, Prop. L; p. 22, Prop. LIII; p. 48.

22. Kepler's *metaphysicis* was omitted by F *1*:65/4; GW *13*:193/174-181, 194-197, 199-203; F *1*:64/18↑-11↑; 65/3-4, 7-8.

NOTES ON CHAPTER VIII

Kepler and Brahe

1. When he entered the University of Jena in the summer semester of 1571, he registered as George Wirn. His surname, like English "weir," suggested a connection with a marsh. After studying Greek, in keeping with the humanistic fashion of the times he translated his surname into Limnaeus. Hence he is recorded as prorector of the University of Jena in the summer semesters of 1593 and 1609 under the name Limnaeus; see *Die Matrikel der Universität Jena*, I (Jena, 1944), xxxvii, xxxix, 366.

2. Foreigners sometimes called the Danish island Hven "Scarlatina," in connection with a legend that it could be bought for as much scarlet cloth as would cover it (Dreyer, p. 89).

3. After leaving Hven, Metius taught at Jena in 1595 (DSB *9*:336/10-12).

4. GW *13*:207/31-208/40; F *1*:194, n. 28/14↑-8↑ (somewhat abbreviated).

5. In a reference to Brahe in the *Cosmographic Mystery*, Kepler said that an opinion of his own was "shared by the noble and most distinguished astronomer Tycho Brahe of Denmark" (GW *1*:76/15-17).

6. GW *13*:154/6-155/24; F *1*:42/10↑-43/7; TB *8*:14/33-15/12.

7. GW *13*:197/2-9; F *1*:43/22-27; TB *8*:44/8-16.

8. Nearly a year after Brahe's death, Kepler told Herwart: "Both before [meeting Tycho] and thereafter, while Tycho was alive and knew about it, I followed the hypotheses of Copernicus (GW *14*:283/24-25). Yet when Brod's Brahe asks Kepler: "What is your decision between Copernicus and me?," Brod's Kepler answers: "I am still undecided" (pp. 161, 163).

9. Despite Brahe's recognition that Copernicus's universe was almost infinite, Marie Boas (Hall) and A. Rupert Hall asserted that Brahe "helped to ... create an unlimited, if not an infinite universe, quite different from the small, tightly bounded universe Copernicus

described" ("Tycho Brahe's System of the World," *Occasional Notes of the Royal Astronomical Society*, 1959, *3*:256/23↑-21↑).

10. The distance from Wandsbek to Hamburg is one-half of a German mile or two conventional miles.

11. GW *13*: #92/72-76, 96-105; F *1*:44/21-24, 22↑-15↑; TB *8*:45/40-46/2, 46/22-32.

12. Kepler's first letter to Ursus, dated 15 November 1595; reprinted from UAH by Scheibel, III, 251 -254; facsimile in *Popular Astronomy*, 1946, *54*:409-410. Brod (pp. 125, 128, 131) misplaced this letter in Ursus's *Chronotheatrum*, of which the author sent a copy to Kepler together with his letter of 29 May 1597. On the other hand, Ursus was very careful not to send Kepler a copy of his *Astronomical Hypotheses*, in which he printed Kepler's first letter to himself.

13. This situation was mistakenly reversed in Roeslin's *Work of God*, where diagram III, p. 54, shows Ursus's Mars intersecting the sun's orbit, while diagram II, p. 53, displaying Mars as encircling the sun without any intersection, is misattributed to Copernicus, but the misattribution is withdrawn on p. 55, where diagram II is assigned to Brahe.

14. GW *13*:200/109-130; F *1*:219/20↑-5↑; TB *8*:46/37-47/15.

15. GW *13*: #92/130-163; F *1*:219/5↑-220/22; TB *8*: 47/15-48/7.

16. List-Bialas, p. 125.

NOTES ON CHAPTER IX

Brahe and Maestlin

1. The Gregorian date corresponding to Julian 21 April is not 31 April (as in F *1*:46/19↑).

2. GW *13*:204/1-8; F *1*:45/19-24; TB *8*:53/8-15.

3. GW *1*:84/36-40; F *1*:27/31-34.

4. GW *13*:204/8-18; F *1*:45/24-32; TB *8*:53/15-25.

5. GW *1*:85/3-9; F *1*:27/19↑-15↑.

6. GW *13*:# 94/18-26; F *1*:45/32-38; TB *8*:53/26-33.

7. GW *13*:205/43-46; F *1*:46/16↑-14↑; TB *8*:55/40-42.

8. F *1*:46/19↑-18↑; TB *8*:433/on 52/10.

9. GW *13*:236/138-150; F *1*:232/last 10 lines.

10. Maestlin's error was repeated by F *1*:219/23↑; F *8*: cxl, left column/12. Kepler's letter was placed "just behind the frontispiece" by Brod (p. 128), still confusing Ursus's *Chronotheatrum* with UFA.

11. GW *13*: #101/150-160; F *1*:232/last line-233/7.

NOTES ON CHAPTER X

Ursus as Imperial Mathematician

1. Gustav E. Pazaurek, *Die Gläsersammlung des nordböhmischen Gewerbe-Museums in Reichenberg* (Leipzig, 1902), p. 9/30-31; Fritz Röver, "Caspar Lehmann aus Uelzen," *Niederdeutsche Beiträge zur Kunstgeschichte*, 1965, *4*:251-268, with the death of Regina, his first wife, dated in 1606 at p. 262/5↑-4↑. Erich Meyer-Heisig, "Caspar Lehmann: Ein Beitrag zur Frühgeschichte des deutschen Glasschnittes," *Anzeiger des germanischen Nationalmuseums Nürnberg*, 1963, pp. 116-131; Servé Minis, "Caspar Lehmann: Glasgraveur aan het hof van Rudolf II," at pp. 191-197 in *Rudolph II and His Court*, Leids Kunsthistorisch Jaarboke, 1982.

2. TB *8*:50/27-51/15.

3. Michael the Brave, voivode of Wallachia; Nicolae Iorga, *Histoire des Roumains de Transylvanie et de Hongrie*, 2nd ed. (Bucharest, 1916), I, 263.

4. Rudolph II's younger brother, Archduke Ernest (1553-1595), had died on 12 February 1595.

5. TB *8*:73/8-31.

6. TB *5*:5-10.

7. Valerie Scho Carey kindly examined for me the University of Michigan's copy of Küster.

8. Wilhelm Norlind, *Tycho Brahe* (Lund, 1970), p. 286.

NOTES ON CHAPTER XI

Kepler and Maestlin

1. GW *13*: #106/3-17; F *1*:91/21-33.
2. GW *1*:407/16↑-14↑; F *8*:688/6.
3. GW *13*:261/465-476; F *1*:233/23-33.
4. Although Kepler says he "dash[ed] off" his letter to Ursus of 15 November 1595, Brod's Kepler declares: "My friends wrote all these letters for me. I never contributed anything but the signature" (p. 132/5↑-4↑). Kepler's *Cosmographic Mystery* was dated 1596, but was not ready for distribution until the following year. Yet Brod mistakenly had Kepler send his letter of 15 November 1595 to Ursus "at the same time" as a presentation copy of the *Cosmographic Mystery*.
5. GW *13*: #106/487-512; F *1*:233/7↑-234/18.
6. GW *13*:275/38-40; F *1*:47/6↑ (abbreviated).
7. GW *13*:276/84-86; F *1*:48/7-9.
8. GW *13*:279/212-213; 280/271.
9. GW *13*:276/86-96; F *1*:48/9-13 (abbreviated).
10. GW *13*: #110/113-122; F *1*:234/21-27.

NOTES ON CHAPTER XII

Kepler, Brahe, and Maestlin

1. Brahe's letter to Kepler of 1/11 April 1598 did not reach the recipient until 8/18 February 1599. Just five days earlier Kepler had received that letter's most significant part, recopied by Maestlin from the copy sent to him by Brahe (GW *13*:289/2-3).
2. GW *13*:286/2-18; F *1*:220/15↑-221/1; TB *8*:141/22-39. "To calumniate one's teacher behind his back" was the purpose of Kepler's first letter to Ursus, as misconceived by Brod (p. 131). But in 1595 Brahe was not yet Kepler's teacher, nor was he so much as mentioned, let alone calumniated, in that letter (GW *13*:48-49; F *1*:218-219).

3. GW *13*:261/480-481; F *1*:233/13↑-12↑.
4. GW *13*:201/150; F *1*:220/12; TB *8*:47/35.
5. GW *13*:286/18-33; F *1*:221/1-16; TB *8*:142/1-16.
6. GW *13*:200/137-138; F *1*:220/2; TB *8*:47/22-23.
7. He has not yet been identified.
8. Kepler wrote *pleraque* (GW *13*:287/66, relying on Kepler's autograph draft, and the scribe's fair copy), not *omnia,* as in Hansch (p. 107/right hand column/24), followed by F*1*:221/5 and TB *8*:143/7.
9. Kepler wrote *videat* (Hansch, p. 107/right hand column/25; GW *13*:287/66; TB *8*:143/7), which was emended to *videas* by F*1*:221/5.
10. Johannes Regiomontanus (1436-1476), *De triangulis omnimodis,* published posthumously (Nuremberg, 1533); translated into English by Barnabas Hughes (Madison, Wisconsin, 1967).
11. Kepler's *anno 94* (G *13*:287/70; F *1*:222/1) was omitted in Hansch (p. 107/right hand column/19) and in TB *8*:143/12.
12. GW *13*: #112/33-72; F *1*:221/16-222/2; TB *8*: 142/16-143/14.
13. Kepler may have been thinking about Diogenes' encounter with Alexander the Great, as told by Plutarch, "Alexander," ch. 14, in his *Parallel Lives*.
14. 9/19 July 1595, Preface to the *Cosmographic Mystery* (GW *1*:11/35-36; 13/17-18); 10/20 July, in a letter to Maestlin of 2 August 1595 (GW *13*:28/ 39-40). A copy of a much later letter from Kepler to David Fabricius dated 1 October 1602, mentioned 17 July 1595 (GW *14*:276/514-515; F *1*:311/15). But the original of this letter to Fabricius is lost, and the surviving copy is defective.
15. This collection of letters has not yet been identified.
16. At the end of his essay *In Praise of the Fly*, Lucian cites the proverb "make an elephant out of a mouse." *Luciani ... opera,* 2nd ed. Dindorf (Paris, 1867), p. 605/2-3.
17. GW *13*: #112/72-98; F *1*:222:2-27; TB *8*:143/14-40.
18. GW *13*:48/4; F *1*:218/20.

19. George Joachim Rheticus (1514-1574), the only disciple of Copernicus during the master's lifetime, wrote the *First Report* (*Narratio prima*; Gdańsk, 1540; Basel, 1541) on Copernicus's *Revolutions*. As we saw in Ch. IX, the third edition of Rheticus's *First Report* was appended by Maestlin to Kepler's *Cosmographic Mystery*. The *First Report* was translated into English in TCT, pp. 107-196, and into French (StC *20*, 1982).

20. Erasmus Reinhold (1511-1553), professor of astronomy at the University of Wittenberg, published the *Prussian Tables* (Tübingen, 1551), whose three additional editions (1561/1562, 1571/1572, 1585) and one incomplete edition (1598) made it a manual very widely used by astronomers during the second half of the sixteenth century (Zinner, #2029, 2270, 2288, 2553, 3200, 3791).

21. Kepler recalled this advice to approach a dangerous enemy soothingly because the proverb referred to the wild bear (*ursus*), whose name his human adversary had adopted.

22. GW *13*: #112/98-128; F *1*:222/27-223/5; TB *8*:143/140-144/28.

23. GW *13*:200/121; F *1*:219/11; TB *8*:47/7.

24. UFA, fol. 38r/#5, sig. K6.

25. GW *13*:289/129-139; F *1*:223/5-16; TB *8*:144/28-39.

26. Stuttgart, Landesbibliothek, Cod. Math. fol. 14a, pp. 65-68.

27. GW *13*:289/140-144; F *1*:223/17-20.

28. Leningrad Observatory, Kepler Manuscripts, V, 259-262.

29. Vienna, Austrian National Library, Cod. 10686/10, 11/pp. 9-10.

30. See the text at n. 31, below.

31. GW *13*:289/2-4; F *1*:48/24 -22 . The expression "imagining that she was flying on a sparrow" was attributed by the augmented edition of Henry Stephanus's *Thesaurus graecae linguae* to "Lys. 724," without explaining who "Lys." was; 3rd ed., VII (Paris, 1848-1854), 883C.

32. GW *13*: #113/4-15; F *1*:48/22 -12 .

33. TB *8*:136/11-15.

34. These 30 German miles correspond to the nearly 150 statute miles from Prague northwest to Wittenberg.

35. GW *13*:292/118-123; F *4*:70/9 -5 .

NOTES ON CHAPTER XIII

Kepler's Analysis of Ursus's "Astronomical Hypotheses"

1. GW *13*: 286/15-17; F *1*:220/3↑-2↑; TB *8*:141/36-38.

2. GW *13*:193/174; F *1*:64/18 .

3. GW *13*:332/28-32; F *1*:284, n. 5/20-24 (abbreviated).

4. GW *13*:339/2-4.

5. GW *13*:341/102-109.

6. GW *13*:341/109-113.

7. Kepler was overcome by the impulse to write to Ursus when he learned that the courier for Prague was about to leave Graz.

8. GW *13*: #123/113-122.

9. GW *13*:342/122-124.

10. Johannes Moller, *Cimbria literata* (Copenhagen, 1744), I, 516/29↑-28↑, 20↑; 517/1-4, 33↑-31↑.

11. Zinner, #3552.

12. Only three times, according to Kepler's letter of 8 December 1598 to Maestlin (GW *13*:261/464, 474, 483; F *1*:233/22, 31, 40).

13. GW *13*:342/124-153.

14. UAH, sig. K2r/right.

15. GW *13*:343/166-168.

16. Brahe's *inversis* (TB *6*:178/41) was misprinted as *universis* in Ursus's reproduction of Brahe's letter (UAH, sig. E4v/2).

17. TB *6*:178/40 - 179/1. In discussing Rothmann's inversion of Copernicus, Brahe "made reference also to Rein-

hold's similar attempt," according to the topsy-turvy paraphrase by Christine Schofield, "The Geoheliocentric Mathematical Hypothesis in Sixteenth-Century Planetary Theory," *British Journal for the History of Science*, 1964, *2*:296/10-11.

NOTES ON CHAPTER XIV

Brahe, Reinhold, and Wittich

1. Printed in the front matter of the first edition of Reinhold's *Prussian Tables* (Tübingen, 1551).

2. Alexandre Birkenmajer, "Le Commentaire inédit d'Erasme Reinhold sur le *De revolutionibus* de Nicolas Copernic," *La Science au seizième siècle*, Colloque international de Royaumont 1-4 juillet 1957 (Paris, 1960), p. 178/12-13.

3. East Berlin, State Library, Latin 2º 391.

4. Facsimile in StC *6*: Plate III, between pp. 56 and 57, and in Owen Gingerich, ed., *The Nature of Scientific Discovery* (Washington, D.C., 1975), p. 438.

5. Reading *Copernico* (facsimile, StC *6*:56-57, Plate III/16), not Copernicae (StC *6*:59/18).

6. Reading *opposito* (Plate III/19), not *oppositio* (StC *6*:59/20).

7. StC *4*:765-766.

8. Zinner, #2466, 2500, 2528, 2589, 2618,2645, 2668, 2681, 2710.

9. TB *3*: 212-216.

10. Valentin Rose, ed., *Die Handschriften-Verzeichnisse der k. Bibliothek zu Berlin*, XIII (Berlin, 1905; Verzeichniss der lateinischen Handschriften, 2te Bd, 3 Abt), pp. 1366-1367, #82, sections 1 and 5; L.A. Birkenmajer, *Mikołaj Kopernik* (Cracow, 1900), pp. 624-629.

11. Pp. 176-177, in *La Science au seizième siècle* (XIV, n. 2). This volume was not "first published in 1957," as in Robert S. Westman, p. 426/ n. 40/3, in Gingerich, ed., *The Nature of Scientific Discovery*.

12. 1566, 1568, 1575, 1598-1599 (Dreyer, pp. 22-23, 29, 83, 271, 276).

13. Owen Gingerich, "Copernicus and Tycho," *Scientific American*, 1973 (December), *229*:99/3rd column/26↑-22↑; Gingerich, "The Astronomy and Cosmology of Copernicus," International Astronomical Union, *Highlights of Astronomy*, 1974, *3*:81-82; Edward Rosen, "Tycho Brahe and Erasmus Reinhold," *Archives Internationales d'Histoire des Sciences*, 1982, *32*:3-8.

14. Gingerich, *Scientific American*, 1973 (December), *229*:99/2nd column/14↑-13↑.

15. *Tychonis Brahei et ad eum doctorum virorum epistolae*, ed. F.R. Friis (Copenhagen, 1876-1886), facing p. VIII; TB *12*:53; *Isis*, 1979, *70*:122, 124, 125, 126 (Figures 1, 5-7).

16. *Editio cimelia Bohemica*, XVI (Prague, 1971), *Nicolai Copernici De revolutionibus orbium coelestium libri sex (editio Basileensis) cum commentariis manu scriptis Tychonis Brahe*, p. 11/4, 23-24.

17. Westman, *Copernican Achievement*, p. 342/6↑-3↑.

18. Duncan Liddel, *Ars medica* (Hamburg, 1607-1608, 1617, 1628), letter of 1 May 1607 from Johannes Caselius to John Craig.

19. *Aeltere Universitäts-Matrikeln*, I, Universität Frankfort a. O., ed. Ernst Friedlaender (Leipzig, 1887; reprint, Osnabrück, 1965; Publicationen aus den k. Preussischen Staatsarchiven, XXXII), 277/#75.

20. Owen Gingerich and Robert S. Westman, "A Reattribution of the Tychonic Annotations in Copies of Copernicus's *De Revolutionibus*," JHA, 1981, *12*:53-54. These annotations are still labeled "Tychonic" only because they were previously misattributed to Tycho by Gingerich and Westman.

21. Liddel, *Ars medica*, Caselius to Craig.

22. William P. D. Wightman, *Science and the Renaissance* (Edinburgh/New York, 1962), II, 66-67/#172.

23. Westman, *Copernican Achievement*, p. 318, Figure 7, and p. 320, Figure 8.

24. NCCW, II, 21-22.

25. TB *13*:316/n. 1; English paraphrase by J.L.E. Dreyer, "On Tycho Brahe's Manual of Trigonometry," *Observatory*, 1916, *39*:129-130.

26. TB *13*:317/upper left corner.

27. TB *13*:308, 319; Edward Rosen, "Render Not Unto Tycho That Which Is Not Brahe's," *Sky and Telescope*, 1981 (June), *61*:476-477.

28. Gingerich, *Scientific American*, *229*, 1973 (December), p. 99/3rd column/37-44; Gingerich, *Highlights of Astronomy*, 1974, *3*:81-82.

29. Facsimiles in Gingerich, *Scientific American*, p. 90, and Westman, p. 312, Figure 6.

30. Westman, p. 311/11↑-9↑.

31. TB *1*:149/30-32.

32. TB *1*:172/37-39.

33. Westman's attempt at a translation (p. 317/2nd extract) omits the crucial word *vere*.

34. Facsimiles in Gingerich, *Scientific American*, p. 100, and Westman, p. 328, Figure 12.

35. TB 7:129/40-130/2.

36. Gingerich, *Scientific American*, p. 101/first column/14-16; *Highlights of Astronomy*, p. 82/ 23-24.

37. Westman, p. 345/6↑-3↑.

38. On the basis of an incorrect reading (TB *1*:xli/2: *ex inspirato*, as against *ex insperato*, TB *4*: 156/29-30), Dreyer mistranslated "by inspiration" (*Tycho Brahe*, Edinburgh, 1890; reprinted, New York, 1963, p. 168/9; *History of the Planetary Systems from Thales to Kepler*, Cambridge, Engl., 1906; reprinted, New York, 1953, p. 363/12-13).

39. TB *4*:156/29-30.

40. Josef Volf, "Tycho Brahe a jeho hvezdárská pozustalost," *Česky Bibliofil*, 1931, *3*:18/6-8 (the late Professor Miroslav Rensky read Volf for me).

41. GW *19*:203/7-8.

42. F. R. Friis, "Tyge Brahe's Haandskrifter i Wien og Prag," *Danske Samlinger*, 1868-1869, *4*:267/7-10.

43. J.A. Hanslik, *Geschichte und Beschreibung der Prager Universitätsbibliothek* (Prague, 1851), p. 274: "The value of the copy in question [Prague facsimile]

is in addition quite exceptionally enhanced by the numerous annotations, discussions, and corrections, and the related mathematical diagrams, inscribed by Tycho Brahe's own hand in the margin;" *Zusätze*, ed. I.J. Hanus (Prague, 1863), p. 9.

44. F.J. Studnička, *Prager Tychoniana* (Prague, 1901), p. 43; B. Prusík, "Tychoniana der Prager k. k. Universitäts-Bibliothek," *Mittheilungen des österreichischen Vereines für Bibliothekswesen*, 1901, *5*:199/#VI; R. Kukula, "Die Tychoniana der Prager K. K. Universitäts-Bibliothek," *Zeitschrift für Bücherfreunde*, 1906-1907, *10*:24/10 -7 ; W. Prandtl, "Die Bibliothek des Tycho Brahe," *Philobiblon, Zeitschrift für Bücherliebhaber*, 1932, *5*:323/#14 (reprinted, Vienna, 1933, p. 11/#14), F. Kleinschnitzová, "Ex bibliotheca Tychoniana Collegii Soc. Jesu Pragae ad S. Clementem," *Nordisk Tidskrift för Bok-och Biblioteksväsen*, 1933, *20*:86/#11; E. Urbánková, *Rukopisy a vzacné tisky pražské Universitní knihovny* (Prague, 1957), p. 72/8-11.

45. Prague facsimile, p. 12/11 -6 .

46. As the date of Wittich's death, TB *6*:356 on 117/2, and DSB, *14*:470/5↑, gave 9 January 1587, repeating Rudolph Wolf, "Beiträge zur Geschichte der Astronomie. 3. Paul Wittich aus Breslau," *Vierteljahrsschrift der astronomischen Gesellschaft*, 1882, *17*: 129, 12 . Wolf cited *Silesia togata*, an unpublished manuscript by Nicholas Henel of Hennefeld (1584-1656). But Henel's fol. 415v (of which a microfilm was kindly provided by Dr. B. Kuzak, director of the library of the University of Wrocław) dates Wittich's death on 5 January 1586.

47. TB *8*:34/4-16. Brahe's presentation copy of his *Astronomiae instauratae mechanica* (Wandsbek, 1598) to Monaw was bought for thirty dollars by the library of the University of Frankfurt on the Oder, whence it passed to the library of the University of Breslau (now Wrocław; Leopold Cohn, "Tycho Brahes Astronomiae instauratae Mechanica von 1598," *Centralblatt fur Bibliothekswesen*, 1903, *20*:279). Monaw's surname was latinized as Monavius. This was misreported as "Moravius" (the man from Moravia) by Bernhard Hasselberg (1848-1922), "Einige Bemerkungen über Tycho Brahes *Astronomiae instauratae mechanica*,"

Vierteljahrsschrift der astronomischen Gesellschaft, 1904, *39*: 184, #12.

48. TB *8*:266/1-6.

49. See the text at Ch. XIV, n. 25, above.

50. P. 12/27.

51. Westman, *Copernican Achievement*, p. 341/17; Edward Rosen, "In Defense of Tycho Brahe," *Archive for History of Exact Sciences*, 1981, *24*:257-265.

52. N. I. Nevskaia, "A Unique Copy of Copernicus's Book," *Voprosy istorii estestvoznania i tekhniki*, 1979, *61-63*:83-86.

53. *Ibid.*, 1980, pp. 103-106, Owen Gingerich, "Annotations in Copernicus's Book."

NOTES ON CHAPTER XV

Ursus's Misunderstanding of Copernicus

1. GW *13*:343/168-170.

2. UAH, sig. A4r/13↑-12↑.

3. UAH, sig. D2, as cited by Kepler in a marginal note.

4. UAH, sig. D2r-v.

5. Copernicus, *Revolutions*, III, 25 (NCCW, II, 169/36-43).

6. GW *13*:343/170-198.

7. GW *13*: #123/198-202.

8. GW *13*:344/205-209.

9. Copernicus, *Revolutions*, III, 22 (NCCW, II, 166/1-2).

10. GW *13*:344/209-212.

11. GW *13*:344/212-222.

12. NCCW, II, 241/47-48; 302/32-35.

13. GW *13*:344/222-223.

14. GW *13*: #123/223-229.

15. GW *13*:345/229-233.
16. GW *13*:345/234-237.
17. GW *13*:345/237-243.

NOTES ON CHAPTER XVI

Ursus's Admission of His Intellectual Theft

1. GW *13*:345/243-247.
2. UAH, sig. F2r.
3. This passage in UAH (sig. F1r) was unfamiliar to Dreyer, who said: "I have not seen this book myself" (p. 273/n. 2). Unaware that Ursus confessed his theft, Dreyer mistakenly declared that "it could not possibly be proved that Reymers had copied the idea of his planetary system from Tycho Brahe" (p. 275/7↑-5↑).

NOTES ON CHAPTER XVII

Kepler's Evaluation of Ursus
as a Mathematician and Astronomer

1. GW *13*:345/248-256.
2. GW *13*: #123/256-275.

NOTES ON CHAPTER XVIII

Ursus's Knowledge of Contemporary
Mathematicians

1. GW *13*:346/276-279.
2. Jacques-Auguste de Thou, *Historiarum sui temporis libri*, Book 129, year 1603 (ed. London, 1733, *6*: 180/25-28).
3. UAH, sig. F3v/6.

4. Bürgi, *Arithmetische und geometrische Progress-Tabulen* (Prague, 1620); reprinted in H. R. Gieswald, *Justus Byrg als Mathematiker* (Danzig, 1856).

5. J.G. Brengger, *Praematurae solis apparitionis in Nova Zembla causa vera* (Strasbourg, 1612).

6. Christopher Clavius, *Astrolabe* (Rome, 1593), p. 3.

7. GW *13*:346/283-285.

8. Later on, in 1612, Brengger published the *Real Reason for the Untimely Appearance of the Sun in Novaya Zembliya* (see Ch. XII, n. 5, above), to which Roeslin added *Precise Instructions for Correctly Managing the Northern Passage to the East Indies* (*Accurata instructio navigationis septentrionalis ad Indias Orientales dextre instituendae*).

9. GW *14*:20/151-153.

10. List-Bialas, pp. 21, 26, 28, 31-32, 38-42, 50, 52, 62-63, 77.

11. Edward Rosen, "The Earliest Translation of Copernicus's 'Revolutions' into German," *Sudhoffs Archiv*, 1982, *66*:301-305.

NOTES ON CHAPTER XIX

Kepler's Preference for Copernicus Over Brahe

1. GW *13*:346/286-288.

2. See Ch. XIV, above, at n. 9.

3. GW *13*:346/288-290, 293-294.

4. NCCW, II, 20/41-43, 26/38-39. Yet Marie Boas and A. Rupert Hall credited Brahe with creating "an unlimited, if not an infinite universe, quite different from the small, tightly bounded universe Copernicus described," "Tycho Brahe's System of the World," *Occasional Papers of the Royal Astronomical Society*, 1959, *3*:256/22↑-21↑.

5. GW *13*:346/294-303.

6. GW *13*:198/51-52; TB *6*:45/17-19; F *1*:44/2-3.

7. GW *13*: #123/306-310.

8. GW *13*:347/310-314.

NOTES ON CHAPTER XX

Kepler's Report to Maestlin about Ursus's *Astronomical Hypotheses*

1. GW *14*:16/2-4; F *1*:70/5↑-3↑ (somewhat abbreviated).
2. GW *14*:39/662-663.
3. GW *14*:55/493-495.
4. GW *14*:44/35-39; F *1*:234/12↑-8↑.
5. UAH, sig. D1r/5-6; GW *14*:44/43-44; F *1*:234/4↑-3↑.
6. GW *14*:44/45-49; F *1*:234/3↑-235/2.
7. UAH, sig. K2r-v.
8. UAH, sig. A3v/21-22; A4r/16↑-13↑; C3r/3-8; D2v/ 15↑ -13↑; E4v/#10; K2r/right.
9. PS, XII, 1; *Claudii Ptolemaei opera*, ed. J.L. Heiberg, I^2 (Leipzig, 1903), 451/6-9.
10. UAH, sig. D2v/7-23.
11. Reading *lemmatii*, with F *1*:235/19, not *lemmatis*, as in GW *14*:44/67, since Copernicus himself used the diminutive *lemmation* (NCCW, II, 436/ on 302/32).
12. UAH, sig. A4r/16↑-13↑; D2r/15-3↑.
13. GW *14*: #132/50-77; F *1*:235/2-28.

NOTES ON CHAPTER XXI

Brahe's Report to Kepler about Ursus

1. GW *14*: #132/50-77; F *1*:235/2-28; Edward Rosen, "Was Kepler Promised the Office of Imperial Mathematician by Emperor Rudolph II?," *Sudhoffs Archive*, 1983.
2. GW *14*:61/80-81.

3. GW *14*:75/519-520.

4. GW *14*:93/170; F *1*:225/32; TB *8*:207/36.

5. GW *14*: #145/2-16; F *1*:223/23-34; TB *8*:203/29-204/5.

6. See, above, Ch. XII, at nn.3, 5, 17, 20.

7. GW *14*:90/16-23; F *1*:223/34-39; TB *8*:204/5-12.

8. UAH, sig. A4r/8-10.

9. GW *14*:90/23-28; F *1*:223/18↑-14↑; TB *8*:204/12-17.

10. F *1*:227-278, n. 3.

11. GW *14*:90/28-31; TB *8*:204/17-20; F *1*:223/14↑-12↑ (abbreviated). Brahe's title, *Books of Astronomical Letters, the First of which Comprises [Certain] Communications* (*Epistolarum astronomicarum libri quorum primus hic ... literas ... complectitur*), is compressed ungrammatically as *Epistolarum astronomicarum liber primum* (!) by Nicholas Jardine, "The Forging of Modern Realism: Clavius and Kepler against the Sceptics," *Studies in History and Philosophy of Science*, 1979, *10*:143, n. 9; 162, n. 56.

12. TB *6*:54-58.

13. TB *6*:61-62.

14. TB *6*:61/41; F *1*:226/22.

15. TB *6*:14/26-29.

16. After 333 years this discrepancy was noticed by Hans Raeder, assistant editor of TB *6* (p. 351, n. 1), and was discussed by him in *Edda*, 1921, *14*:112-115.

17. TB *6*:179/21-22; F *1*:226/32-33.

18. TB *6*:183/13-15.

19. TB *6*:362/2-3, 2↑.

20. TB *9*:89/18-20, 91/16.

21. TB *6*:179/22; F *1*:226/32-33.

22. Jacob Kurtz (†1594), Vice-Chancellor of the Holy Roman Empire, obtained the imperial license of 13 June 1590 for Brahe's *Astronomiae instauratae mechanica*, which included his letter to Brahe of 28 June 1590 (TB *5*:119-122). After Kurtz's death, his widow sold their house in Prague for $10,000 to the emperor, who gave it to Brahe as his residence. When Brahe took possession

of it on 25 February 1601, he made room for Kepler and his family.

23. GW *14*:90/31-49; TB *8*:204/20-38; F *1*:223/12 - 224/1.

24. TB *5*:121/34.

25. UAH, sig. I3v/2.

26. MS Smith 77; TB *5*:324 on 121/34.

27. UAH, sig. I3v/15-23, 27-29.

28. GW *14*: #145/49-55; F *1*:224/1-6; TB *8*:204/38-205/2.

29. This individual has not yet been identified.

30. GW *14*:91/55-90; F *1*:224/6-33; TB *8*:205/2-38.

31. Brahe gives Benátky's distance from Prague as 5 German miles (= 20 statute miles). Benátky, a rural resort, lay about 24 statute miles northeast of Prague, the imperial capital. Yet Longberg's *Benachia* (Benátky) was misidentified with Prague by N. M. Swerdlow, *Proceedings of the American Philosophical Society*, 1973, *117*: 431/right/19↑.

32. GW *14*: #145/242-263; TB *8*:209/26-210/6; F *1*:47/32-46 (omitting the reference to Blotius); F *8*:717/n.*/11-19 (compressed even further).

33. GW *14*: #149/2-8; TB *8*:215/25-31.

34. GW *14*:99/7-10.

35. GW *14*:107/2-17; TB *8*:246/6-23; F *8*:716/11-19 (somewhat abbreviated).

36. GW *14*:119/7-10.

37. GW *14*: #168/9-26, 100-101; F *1*:71/2↑-72/16, 73/6-7.

NOTES ON CHAPTER XXII

A Witness for Brahe: Rodolphe Méhérenc

1. These deliberately vague statements hint at the dismal future awaiting the Protestants in France and Styria alike.

2. Charles de Danzay (1508/09-1589) was born on his family's hereditary estate in Danzay, near Poitiers.

Francis I sent him to Strasbourg to learn German, so that he could serve France in war with the Germans or in negotiations with them. Turning Protestant, he was appointed to be the French ambassador to Denmark, where he became friendly with Brahe. In his *Astronomiae instauratae mechanica*, Brahe reported about Uraniburg Observatory:

> As soon as Danzay learned that this building was to be constructed, of his own accord he offered to lay the first cornerstone here. He promptly arranged to have the following inscription carved on a certain reddish stone:
>
>> In the Reign of Frederick II in Denmark Charles de Danzay of Aquitaine, ambassador of the king of France, erected this votive stone for this building, constructed by the noble lord Tycho Brahe of Knudstrup, in accordance with the king's decree, for the study of science and especially of the stars, to serve as a memorial and be a happy omen.

In the year 1576, 8 August (TB *5*:143/11-23)

Though Brahe's observatory is gone, a fragment of Danzay's cornerstone was found in the wall of a house on Hven, and is preserved in the historical museum of Lund, Sweden. It shows that the original plan was to lay the cornerstone on 1 August. But the ceremony actually took place a week later, under more favorable astrological auspices (TB *5*:326 on 143/23).

The memorial published by the University of Copenhagen on the occasion of Danzay's funeral gives the date of his death as 12 October 1589 (*Oversigt over det kongelike danske videnskabernes selskabs forhandlinger*, 1897, p. 667/last line - p. 668/8). Since Brahe says that Danzay died in his 81st year (TB *5*:143/9-10), he was born either in 1508, after 12 October, or in 1509, before 12 October.

3. *Stella caudata*; see Ch. I, paragraph 2.

4. GW *14*: #150.

NOTES ON CHAPTER XXIII

Two Other Witneses for Brahe: Hansen and Walter

1. GW *14*:96/284-290; TB *8*:210/28-35; F *1*:225/3↑-226/3.
2. TB 7:359/31; TB *8*:102/13, 150/12, 210/30-31; see also TB *14*:45/5.
3. As in GW *14*: p. 469 on line 286, p. 516.
4. He is alphabetized by his given name in TB *8*:454 and TB *15*:16.
5. As in Poul Georg Lindhardt, *Fem Aalborg-bisper* (Aalborg, 1954), pp. 14, 258. Hansen was bishop of Aalborg from 1609 to 1642.
6. TB *9*:44/11.
7. TB *9*:49/49.
8. TB *9*:53/31, 58/9.
9. TB *9*:84/25-26.
10. As in TB *14*:45/7.
11. TB *12*:197.
12. TB *12*:268.
13. TB *13*:388-389.
14. TB *7*:359/37.
15. TB *12*:371.
16. TB *13*:118-119.
17. TB *8*:84/8-9; 102/12-13; 262/8-9.
18. Hansen's syntax requires *ratio*, not *rationem*.
19. Martial, I, 52/9.
20. *κραληρ κακων* (kraler kakon), with Hansen misplacing the accent over the *ρ* in this Byzantine loan word borrowed from Slavic.
21. Intending to write *confugeret*, Hansen started with "cuo," which he did not erase, but immediately marked as a mistake (*mendum*).

22. Trying to write this word in Greek, Hansen mistakenly put "y" where is required.

23. Since Hansen arrived in Hven in 1586, he was present while *Stella caudata* was being printed.

24. Dr. Martha List, Kepler Commission, Bavarian Academy of Sciences, kindly provided a photocopy of Hansen's letter, the original of which is in Vol. V, fol. 301v, of the Kepler manuscripts, formerly in Pulkovo, now in Leningrad. F *1*:230/18-9† printed a curtailed and rewritten version; GW *14*:469 on line 286 mistakenly described this letter from Hansen to Brahe as "previously unpublished."

25. TB *14*:44/26. In Dreyer, *Tycho Brahe*, read *pastorem*, not *pastorum* (pp. 275, 382).

26. The uncertain reading in F *1*:231/31 was corrected in TB *8*:442/1. Bygholm was Lange's residence as governor of East Jutland.

27. F *1*:230/6†-231/6†. Walter's affidavit was mistakenly described as "likewise previously unpublished" (GW *14*:469 on line 291).

28. GW *14*: #145/293-298; TB *8*:210/37-43; F *1*:226/5-9.

29. Here Brahe echoes Jerome's *Epistles*, I, 7; *Corpus scriptorum ecclesiasticorum latinorum, 54*, ed. I. Hilberg (Vienna/Leipzig, 1910), 30/1-2.

30. TB *8*:180/35-181/18.

NOTES ON CHAPTER XXIV

A Kepler-Ursus Plot Against Brahe?

1. This clue identifies Brahe's unnamed agent at the imperial court as Tengnagel, who married Brahe's second daughter Elizabeth (†1613) on 17 June 1601.

2. Brahe calls him "Mecker," and in the Dedication of his *Ephemerides* on 1 November 1616 Kepler states that his appointment as Imperial Mathematician by Emperor Matthias was executed by "Helfrich von Meckaw, Privy Councillor and High Chamberlain" (F 7:480/14-15). Leonhard Helfried von Meggau (1577-1644) was one of Matthias' most trusted associates; *Allgemeine deutsche Biographie*, XXI (Berlin, 1970; reprint

of the 1885 edition), 181.

3. TB *8*:281/16-282/38.
4. F *8*:728/9↑-8↑.
5. TB *8*:299/34-37.

NOTES ON CHAPTER XXV

Brahe's Statement to Háyek Against Ursus

1. See Ch. V, above, before n. 32.
2. TB 7:321/11. Presumably the month and day were included in the copy which was made later for transmission to Háyek, together with the postscript.
3. Lange became engaged to Sophia Brahe (1556-1643) in 1592, but the marriage did not take place until 1602.
4. See, above, Ch. XVIII, n. 11.
5. See, above, Ch. V.
6. Not in this letter, as published. Gellius, a son of the Hollander, Jan Sasgers (Sascerides), was born in Copenhagen in 1562. About 1581 he went to Hven, and left in 1588 (TB *9*:62/42, 63/46). In the list of Tycho's pupils, he is #4, while #21 is his younger brother, David, who remained in Uraniburg only half a year (TB *14*: #69/4, 21).
7. Duncan Liddel (1561-1613) spent five days on Hven in 1587, from 24 June to 29 June (TB *9*:55/3, 11).
8. Brahe compares Ursus with the city of Troy on the night when the Greeks emerged from the Trojan Horse (*Aeneid*, II, 265).
9. Brahe quotes from Vergil, *Eclogues*, III, 93.
10. TB 7:321/14-326/37.

NOTES ON CHAPTER XXVI

Kepler, Maestlin, Brahe, and Herwart

1. GW *14*: #175/2-10, 30-44, 47-56, F *1*:54/15↑-55/7, 55/10-19; facsimile, F *2*:12-13.

2. GW *14*: #174; TB *8*:352/23-30; F *1*:232/29↑-20↑ (somewhat abbreviated).

3. GW *14*:477 on #174, uncritically relying on an earlier editor of three previously unpublished Kepler-Herwart letters (Edward Rosen, "Kepler's Defense of Tycho against Ursus"), *Popular Astronomy*, 1946, *54*:411, n. 21).

4. GW *14*: #176; TB *8*:354/24-35, 354/36-357/11.

5. Munich, State Library, Cod. lat. 1607, pp. 350-374; see Ch. XIII, XV, above.

6. GW *14*:165/161-168; F *3*:49/19↑-9↑.

7. GW *14*:157/57-71; F *2*:13/28-38.

8. GW *14*:158/13-17; F *1*:55/8↑-3↑.

9. GW *14*:202/2-4; F *3*:50/7-9.

10. GW *14*:208/243-245; F *3*:54/15↑-13↑.

NOTES ON CHAPTER XXVII

Kepler's "Quarrel Between Tycho and Ursus Over Hypotheses"

1. Reading *quidam* with F *1*:281/9 , not *quidem* with TB *8*:447 on 343/35.

2. GW *14*:169/21; F *8*:741/5, n. *. The code was deciphered for Frisch by Otto Struve (1819-1905), director of the Pulkovo Observatory.

3. GW *14*:225/71-72.

4. GW *14*:480 on 187/21.

5. GW *14*:225/66-67.

6. F *1*:284/12.

7. F *1*:281/last 10 lines.

8. Martianus Capella, *Marriage of Philology and Mercury* (VIII, 857): "Mercury and Venus ... locate the center of their circles in the sun." The expression *conversas absides* (opposite circles), however, was misattributed by Kepler to Capella, although it actually

occurs in Pliny's *Natural History*, II, 14, 72. Kepler failed to notice that Copernicus lumped Capella with "certain other Latin writers," to whom, and not to Capella by himself, Copernicus attributes *conversas absides*.

9. NCCW, II, 20/14-18.

10. Copernicus believed that the planets were moved by real spheres, but these real spheres interpenetrated one another, like intersecting beams of light.

11. A paraphrase of NCCW, II, 20/42-45.

12. Not for Herwart, as in TB *8*:447 on 343/35/3. Kepler began his "Quarrel" by saying he would try to recall what he had written to Herwart on 20/30 May 1599. But that letter is substantially different from the "Quarrel," which Kepler wrote for Tengnagel in March 1600.

13. F *1*:282/1-284/13.

NOTES ON CHAPTER XXVIII

The Death of Ursus

1. GW *14*:147/68-75; TB *8*:342/5-12.

2. GW *14*:148/129-136; TB *8*:343/25-32; F *1*:232/4-10.

3. GW *14*:137/12-13; F *1*:284/31-32.

4. Their identity has not yet been determined.

5. GW *14*: #173/136-144; TB *8*:343/32-41; F *1*:232/11-17.

6. GW *14*: #174/7; TB *8*:352/21; F *1*:232/26↑-25↑.

7. Reprinted in Pierre Gassendi, *Tychonis Brahei ... vita* (Paris, 1654), p. 268/2-15; (The Hague, 1655), p. 231/7-19. Kepler's *Elegy on the Death of Tycho Brahe* followed Jesenský's *Oration* (1654 ed., pp. 273-278; 1655 ed., pp. 235-240). TB *14*:238/40-239/1.

8. Johannes Moller, *Cimbria literata* (Copenhagen, 1744), I, 515/7-8.

9. GW *14*:149/144-151; TB *8*:343/41-344/5; F *1*:232/11-21.

10. TB *14*:209/#203.
11. GW *14*:149/151-153; TB *8*: 344/5-7; F *1*:232/22-23.
12. Dreyer, *Tycho Brahe*, p. 273/n. 2/last 2 lines.
13. GW *14*:149/153-161; TB *8*:344/7-16; F *1*:232/23-29.
14. TB *8*:334/17-27.
15. TB *8*:371/11-28.
16. Moller, *Cimbria literata*, I, 515/8; F *1*:218/6-7.
17. TB *8*:371/29-372/10.
18. In 1590 Rothmann arrived on 1 August and left on 1 September (TB *9*:89/18-20; 91/16). He did not stay seven weeks, as in Friedrich Wilhelm Strieder, *Grundlage zu einer hessischen Gelehrten- und Schriftsteller-Geschichte*, XII (Kassel, 1799), 123/1-4, or "about seven weeks," as in Rudolf Wolf, "Astronomische Mittheilungen #32," *Vierteljahrsschrift der naturforschenden Gesellschaft in Zürich*, 1872, *17*:390/n.13/6.
19. Johann Friedrich Weidler, *Historia astronomiae* (Wittenberg, 1741), p. 375/3-4, repeated in Johann Christian Götze, *Die Merckwürdigkeiten der k. Bibliothek zu Dressden* (Dresden, 1743-1746), III, 553, and in F *1*:286/28.
20. Strieder, XII, 121-122.
21. TB *8*:182/29-39.
22. Strieder, XII, 128.
23. *Album academiae Vitebergensis*, II (Halle, 1894), 255/b37. Bruce T. Moran published numerous corrections of his article "Christoph Rothmann, the Copernican Theory, and Institutional and Technical Influences on the Criticism of Aristotelian Cosmology," *Sixteenth Century Journal*, 1982, *13*:85-108, on a loose sheet in that *Journal*'s spring issue of 1983. But Moran did not correct his misstatement (p. 86) that "Sometime during the late 1560s or early 1570s Rothmann arrived at the University of Wittenberg." Nor did Moran correct his misdating (p. 85) of Rothmann's death as "c. 1650," although Rothmann's *Bericht von der Tauffe* (1608) was posthumous. Nor did Moran correct his misdescription (p. 87) of the equant as "the point around which the planet maintains uniform angular velocity," whereas that uni-

form angular velocity is maintained by the center of the planet's epicycle, not by the planet itself.

24. TB *8*:183/40-184/5.

25. TB *8*:372/10-16.

26. List-Bialas, pp. 108-109, citing Vienna, Hofkammer-Archiv, Hoffinanzindices, Gedenkbuch, 1600, fol. 275v.

NOTES ON CHAPTER XXIX

The Death of Brahe

1. Willebrord Snel, *Coeli et siderum in eo errantium observationes Hassiacae* (Leiden, 1618), pp. 83-84.

2. Dreyer, *Tycho Brahe*, p. 310, n. 1, pp. 386-387; TB *13*:283.

3. TB *10*:3/1-14.

4. GW *3*:89/10-11; F *3*:193/15↑-13↑.

5. GW *14*:217/13-15.

6. Heinrich Rantzau, *Catalogus imperatorum, regum ac principum qui astrologicam artem amarunt* (Antwerp, 1580), p. 56.

7. GW *14*:217/40-41.

8. Wilhelm Seelman, "George Rollenhagen," *Geschichts-Blätter für Stadt und Land Magdeburg* (Mitteilungen des Vereins für Geschichte und Altertumskunde des Herzogtums und Erzstifts Magdeburg), 1889, *24*:107/9↑-5↑.

9. *Ibid.*, pp. 84-85.

NOTES ON CHAPTER XXX

Kepler's *Defense of Tycho Against Ursus*

1. GW *14*:281/22-24; F *1*:235/9↑-7↑.

2. GW *14*:334/641-643; F *1*:235/7↑-3↑. E. Rosen, "Was

Kepler Promised the Office of Imperial Mathematician by Emperor Rudolph II?," *Sudhoffs Archiv*, 1983.

3. *Philosophical Transactions*, 1674; reprint, New York, 1963; *9*:31.

4. GW *14*:276/534.

5. GW *15*:139/199-200; F *3*:34/5↑-4↑.

6. GW *15*:139/193-195; F *3*:34/10↑-8↑. Here Kepler recalls that he "wrote against Ursus on Tycho's orders" (*jubente Tychone*). Earlier, however, in the Preface to the *Defense* he explained: "I had in the first instance volunteered to transfer this task to myself from Tycho Brahe's shoulders." In either case, whether Kepler obeyed an order by Brahe or initiated the project himself, there were no "protracted and tortuous negotiations through which Kepler became committed to the writing of the *Apologia*" [*Defense*], as imagined by Jardine (Ch. XXI, n. 11), 143, n. 10. According to Jardine, "a full account" of those supposed negotiations "is given by" F, I, 217-235. Those nineteen pages say nothing about negotiations. Instead, F, I, 235/29-30, refers in fifteen words to Brahe's demand (*postulatum*) and Kepler's reluctant acceptance (*aegre subiit negotium*).

7. Ch. XXVI, before n. 6.

8. GW *14*:165/161-162; F *3*:49/16↑-15↑.

9. F *8*:738/20.

10. GW *15*:139/201-204; F *3*:34/2↑-35/2.

11. See, above, Ch. XII, after n. 2.

12. See, above, Ch. XII, at n. 3. Kepler's letter to Maestlin of 19/29 August 1599 regarded it "as almost certain that from the very start I mentioned Tycho" (Ch. XX, n. 6).

13. See, above, Ch. XII, from n. 1 to n. 28.

14. GW *4*:105/3-9; F *1*:504/10↑-4↑.

15. GW *4*:105/10-14; F *1*:504/3↑-505/3.

SOURCES OF THE ILLUSTRATIONS

BIBLIOGRAPHY

Adam, Melchior, *Vitae Germanorum philosophorum*. Heidelberg, 1615.

Aeltere Universitäts-Matrikeln, I, Frankfurt a. O., ed. Ernst Friedlaender. Leipzig, 1887; reprint Osnabrück, 1965.

Album academiae Vitebergensis, I, ed. K. E. Förstemann. Leipzig, 1841; II, eds. Otto Hartwig and Gotthold. Halle, 1894.

Anon., *The Church History of England from the Year 1500, to the Year 1688*, 3 vols. Brussels, 1737-1742.

Birkenmajer, Alexandre, "Le Commentaire inédit d'Erasme Reinhold sur le *De revolutionibus* de Nicolas Copernic," *La Science au seizième siècle* (Collogue international de Royaumont 1-4 juillet 1957). Paris, 1960.

Birkenmajer, Ludwik Antoni, *Mikołaj Kopernik*. Cracow, 1900.

Blumhof, J. G. L., *Vom alten Mathematiker Conrad Dasypodius*. Göttingen, 1796.

Boas-Hall, Marie and A. Rupert Hall, "Tycho Brahe's System of the World," *Occasional Notes of the Royal Astronomical Society*, 1959, *3*:257-263.

Brengger, J. G., *Praematurae solis apparitionis in Nova Zembla causa vera*. Strasbourg, 1612.

Bürgi, Jost, *Arithmetische und geometrische Progress-Tabulen*. Prague, 1620.

Clavius, Christopher, *Astrolabe*. Rome, 1543.

Die jüngere Matrikel der Universitat Leipzig 1559-1809, I, ed. Georg Erler. Leipzig, 1909.

Dreyer, J. L. E., *History of the Planetary Systems from Thales to Kepler*. Cambridge, England, 1906; reprinted as *A History of Astronomy from Thales to Kepler*. New York, 1953.

______, "On Tycho Brahe's Manual of Trigonometry," *Observatory*, 1916, *39*:129-130.

Duhem, Pierre, *Sozein ta phainomena*. Paris, 1908; English translation by E. Doland and C. Maschler, *To Save the Phenomena*. University of Chicago Press, 1969.

Epistolae ad J. Kepplerum, ed. M. G. Hansch. Leipzig, 1718.

Favaro, Antonio, *Carteggio inedito di Ticone Brahe... con G. A. Magini*. Bologna, 1886.

Friis, F. R., "Tyge Brahe's Haandskrifter i Wien og Prag," *Danske Samlinger*, 1868-1869.

Gassendi, Pierre, *Tychonis Brahei... vita*. Paris, 1654; The Hague, 1655.

Gerhardt, C. J., *Geschichte der Mathematik in Deutschland*. Munich, 1877; reprint, New York/London, 1965.

Gingerich, Owen, "Copernicus and Tycho," *Scientific American*, 1973 (December), *229*:86-101.

______, "The Astronomy and Cosmology of Copernicus," *Highlights of Astronomy*, 1974, *3*:67-85.

______, ed., *The Nature of Scientific Discovery*. Washington, D.C., 1975.

______, "Annotations in Copernicus's Book," *Voprosy istorii estestvoznania i tekhniki*, 1980, pp. 103-106.

Gingerich, Owen and Robert S. Westman, "A Reattribution of the Tychonic Annotations in Copies of Copernicus's *De Revolutionibus*," *Journal for the History of Astronomy*, 1981, *12*:53-54.

Götze, Christian, *Die Merckwürdigkeiten der k. Bibliothek zu Dressden*, III. Dresden, 1743-1746.

Hanslik, J. A., *Geschichte und Beschreibung der Prager Universitätsbibliothek*. Prague, 1851.

Hoffman, Gottfried Ernst, *Geschichte Schleswig-Holsteins*, V. Neumünster, 1972.

Iorga, Nicolae, *Histoire des Roumains de Transylvanie et de Hongrie*, I, 2nd ed. Bucharest, 1916.

Kamphausen, Alfred, Nis Rudolf Nissen, and Erich Wohlenberg, *Ditmarschen: Geschichte und Bild einer Landschaft*. Heide in Holstein, 1968.

Kepler, Johannes, *The Secret of the Universe*, English translation of *Mysterium cosmographicum* by A. M. Duncan. New York, 1981.

Kleinschnitzová, Flora, "Ex bibliotheca Tychoniana Collegii Soc. Jesu Pragae ad S. Clementem," *Nordisk Tidskrift för Bok-och Biblioteksväsen* XX, 1933.

Liddel, Duncan, *Ars medica.* Hamburg, 1607-1608, 1617, 1628.

Luciani... opera, 2nd ed. Paris, 1867.

Mackensen, Ludolf v., *Die erste Sternwarte Europas.* Munich, 1979.

Magini, Giovanni Antonio, *Novae coelestium orbium theoricae congruentes cum observationibus N. Copernici.* Venice, 1589.

Moller, Johannes, *Cimbria literata,* I. Copenhagen, 1744.

Moran, Bruce T., "Christoph Rothmann, the Copernican Theory, and Institutional and Technical Influences on the Criticism of Aristotelian Cosmology," *Sixteenth Century Journal,* 1982, *13*:85-108.

Nevskaia, Nina I., "A Unique Copy of Copernicus's Book," *Voprosy istorii estestvoznania i tekhniki,* 1979, *61-63*:83-86.

Prusík, B., "Tychoniana der Prager k. k. Universitäts-Bibliothek," *Mittheilungen des österr. Vereines für Bibliothekswesen* V. Vienna, 1901.

Rantzau, Heinrich, *Catalogus imperatorum, regum ac principum qui astrologicam artem amarunt.* Antwerp, 1580.

Regiomontanus, Johannes, *De triangulis omnimodis.* Nuremberg, 1533; English translation by Barnabas Hughes, *Regiomontanus on Triangles.* University of Wisconsin Press, 1967.

Reinhold, Erasmus, *Prutenicae tabulae coelestium motuum.* Tübingen, 1551.

Roeslin, Helisaeus, *De opere Dei creationis.* Frankfurt, 1597.

Rosen, Edward, "Kepler's Defense of Tycho against Ursus," *Popular Astronomy,* 1946, *54*:405-412.

______, "In Defense of Tycho Brahe," *Archive for History of Exact Sciences,* 1981, *24*:257-265.

______, "Render Not Unto Tycho That Which Is Not Brahe's," *Sky and Telescope,* 1981 (June), 61:476-477.

______, "The Earliest Translation of Copernicus's 'Revolutions' into German," *Sudhoffs Archiv,* 1982, *61*:301-305.

______, "Tycho Brahe and Erasmus Reinhold," *Archives Internationales d'Histoire des Sciences,* 1982, *32*:3-7.

______, "Brod's Brahe: Fact vs. Fiction," *Sudhoffs Archiv,* 1982, *66*:70-78.

Schard, Simon, *Rerum germanicarum scriptores varii,* III, ed. Hieronymus Thomae. Giessen, 1673.

Snel, Willebrord, *Coeli et siderum in eo errantium observationes Hassiacae.* Leiden, 1618.

Strieder, Friedrich Wilhelm, *Grundlage zu einer hessischen Gelehrten-und-Schriftsteller Geschichte*, XII. Kassel, 1799.

Strobel, Adam Gauthier, *Histoire du Gymnase protestant de Strasbourg.* Strasbourg, 1838.

Studnička, F. J., *Prager Tychoniana.* Prague, 1901.

Swerdlow, Noel M., "The Derivation and First Draft of Copernicus's Planetary Theory: A Translation of the Commentariolus with Commentary," *Proceedings of the American Philosophical Society*, 1973, *117*:423-512.

Urbánková, Emma, *Rukopisy a vzácne tisky pražské universitní knihovny*. Prague, 1957.

Ursus, *Geodaesia Ranzoviana.* Leipzig, 1583.

Volf, Josef, "Tycho Brahe a jeho hvezdárská pozustalost," *Česky Bibliofil*, 1931, *3*.

Weidler, J. F., *Historia astronomiae.* Wittenberg, 1741.

Westman, Robert S., *The Copernican Achievement.* Berkeley / London, 1975.

Wightman, William P. D., *Science and the Renaissance*, II. Edinburgh / New York, 1962.

Witte, Henning, *Diarium biographicum.* Danzig, 1688.

INDEX